Practice Papers for SQA Exams

Standard Grade | Credit

Chemistry

Text © 2009 Sandy Macfarlane
Design and layout © 2009 Leckie & Leckie

01/150609

ISBN 978-1-84372-766-8

Published by
Leckie & Leckie Ltd, 4 Queen Street, Edinburgh, EH2 1JE
Tel: 0131 220 6831 Fax: 0131 225 9987
enquiries@leckieandleckie.co.uk   www.leckieandleckie.co.uk

A CIP Catalogue record for this book is available from the British Library.

Leckie & Leckie Ltd is a division of Huveaux plc.

Questions and answers in this book do not emanate from SQA. All of our entirely new and original Practice Papers have been written by experienced authors working directly for the publisher.

About this Book

Layout of the Book

This book contains practice exam papers, which mirror the actual SQA exam as much as possible. The layout, paper colour and question level are all similar to the actual exam that you will sit, so that you are familiar with what the exam paper will look like.

The answer section is at the back of the book. Each answer contains a worked out answer or solution so that you can see how the right answer has been arrived at. The answers also include practical tips on how to tackle certain types of question, details of how marks are awarded and advice on just what the examiners will be looking for.

Revision advice is provided in this introductory section of the book, so please read on!

How to Use this Book

The Practice Papers can be used in two main ways:

1. You can complete an entire practice paper as preparation for the final exam. If you would like to use the book in this way, you can complete the practice paper under exam-style conditions by setting yourself a time for each paper and answering it as well as possible without using any references or notes.

   Alternatively, and I would suggest that this is the **best** technique, you can answer the practice paper questions as a revision exercise, using your notes, Success Guide or revision notes to produce a model answer. Your teacher may mark these for you.

2. You can use the Topic Index on pages 5–6 to find all the questions within the book that deal with a specific topic. This allows you to focus specifically on areas that you particularly want to revise or, if you are mid-way through your course, it lets you practise answering exam-style questions for just those topics that you have studied.

Remember:

Keep a note of the topics you are finding difficult on the table provided and get help with these.

Revision Advice

Work out a revision timetable for each week's work in advance – remember to cover all of your subjects and to leave time for homework and breaks. For example:

Day	6pm–6.45pm	7pm–8pm	8.15pm–9pm	9.15pm–10pm
Monday	Homework	Homework	English revision	**Chemistry** revision
Tuesday	Maths revision	Physics revision	Homework	Free
Wednesday	Geography revision	Modern Studies revision	English revision	French revision
Thursday	Homework	Maths revision	**Chemistry** revision	Free
Friday	Geography revision	French revision	Free	Free
Saturday	Free	Free	Free	Free
Sunday	Modern Studies revision	Maths revision	**Chemistry** revision	Homework

Make sure that you have at least one evening free a week to relax, socialise and re-charge your batteries. It also gives your brain a chance to process the information that you have been feeding it all week.

Arrange your study time into one-hour or 30-minute sessions, with a break between sessions e.g. 6 pm–7 pm, 7.15 pm–7.45 pm, 8 pm–9 pm.

Try to start studying as early as possible in the evening when your brain is still alert and be aware that the longer you put off starting, the harder it will be to start!

Study a different subject in each session, except for the day before an exam.

Do something different during your breaks between study sessions – have a cup of tea, or listen to some music. Don't watch TV or go on the computer during these breaks or the 15 minutes may expand into 30 minutes or longer.

Have your class notes and any textbooks available for your revision to hand as well as plenty of blank paper, a pen, calculator etc. The whole point of the revision is to find out what you cannot do and look up the various notes to learn how to do it before the exam. You may like to make keyword sheets like the chemistry example below:

Keyword	Meaning
electrolysis	The decomposition of an ionic substance by electricity
condensation	Joining two substances by removing water
dehydration	The removal of water from a compound

Finally forget or ignore all or some of the advice in this section if you are happy with your present way of studying. Everyone revises differently, so find a way that works for you!

Transfer Your Knowledge

As well as using your class notes and textbooks to revise, these practice papers will also be a useful revision tool as they will help you to get used to answering exam-style questions. You may find as you work through the questions that they refer to an example that you haven't come across before. Don't worry! You should be able to transfer your knowledge of a topic or theme to a new example. The enhanced answer section at the back will demonstrate how to read and interpret the question to identify the topic being examined and how to apply your course knowledge in order to answer the question successfully.

In the Exam

If there is something that you find difficult to remember, as soon as the exam starts turn to the back page and make a note of it.

i.e. you will be asked to do a calculation so get down the equations

$$n = cxv \quad \text{and} \quad n = m/gfm$$

Each mark should take roughly 1½ minutes. Therefore after 15 minutes you should have covered roughly 10 marks. Section A should take roughly 30 minutes. Watch your time and pace yourself carefully. If you are going too fast, slow yourself down.

Be clear before the exam what the instructions are likely to be e.g. in section A circle the correct responses in the grids provided. The practice papers will help you to become familiar with the exam's instructions.

Read the question thoroughly before you begin to answer it – make sure you know exactly what the question is asking you to do.
Ask yourself:
What am I being asked?
Will a formula help me to answer? (i.e. $n = cxv$)
Will the data booklet help me to answer? (e.g. page 4 gives the formula and charges for complicated ions)

If you do not recognise what the question is about, look to see if it is problem solving: there will be something in the question to help you.

And finally USE THE DATA BOOKLET: it has lots of information which can help you work out some answers.

Good luck!

Topic Index

	Exam A	Exam B	Exam C	Exam D	Questions I found difficult or need help with
1. Chemical Reactions	2	16(c), 16(d)			
2. Speed of Reactions	4, 13	2(a), 13	3		
3. Atoms and the Periodic table	1(a), 11	1(a), 1(b), 10(a)	1, 10(a), 10(b), 10(e), 12(a), 12(b), 12(c)	1	
4. How Atoms Combine	15	10(b)	2(a), 10(c), 10(d)	7(a)	
5. Fuels	3	7	11(a), 11(b)	2, 9(d)	
6. Structure & Reactions of Hydrocarbons	6, 12	3(a), 3(c), 11(b), 15	11(c), 13(a), 13(b), 19	5(b), 5(c), 10, 15	
7. Properties of Substances	1(c), 10, 19(a), 19(b), 19(c)(i), 19(c)(iii)	1(c), 6, 20	7, 14(a)	7(b), 7(c)	
8. Acids and Alkalis	5, 7, 14(d)	3(b), 14(a), 16(b)	2(b), 4	4, 9(c), 12(d)	
9. Reactions of Acids	9, 20	5, 16(a), 18(b)	6, 16	5(a), 14(d)	
10. Making Electricity	8, 19(c)(ii)	2(b), 4, 19	8	3, 6(b), 12(a), 12(b), 12(c), 12(e), 12(f)	
11. Metals	21	18(a), 18(c), 18(d)	5, 15, 17	8, 9(a), 9(b), 11(a), 13(b)	
12. Corrosion	16	8	9	13(a), 13(c)	
13. Plastics & Synthetic Fibres	17	12	13(c)	11(b)	
14. Fertilisers	1(b), 18	14(b), 17	14(c)	14(b)	
15. Carbohydrates & related Substances	14(a), 14(b), 14(c)	9, 11(a)	18	6(a), 14(a), 14(c)	

Practice Exam A

Chemistry   Standard Grade: Credit

Practice Papers For SQA Exams	Time allowed: 1 hour 30 minutes	**Exam A** **Credit Level**

Fill in these boxes:

Name of center

Town

Forename(s)

Surname

Try to answer all of the questions in the time allowed.

Write your answers in the spaces provided, including all of your working.

Full marks will only be awarded where your answer includes any relevant working.

You will find necessary data in the Standard Grade and Intermediate 2 SQA Data Booklet.

You must do your rough work in this exam book – but it must be clearly crossed out.

Leckie×Leckie
Scotland's leading educational publishers

1. The following grid contains metals found in the Periodic Table.

A	B	C
lithium	iron	aluminium
D	E	F
sodium	platinum	lead

(a) Identify the **two** transition metals.

A	B	C
D	E	F

(b) Identify the metal which is used as a catalyst in the Ostwald Process for the production of nitric acid.

A	B	C
D	E	F

(c) Identify the metal which has the lowest density.

You may wish to use the data booklet to help you.

A	B	C
D	E	F

(3)

KU PS

1

1

1

2. Fizzy drinks can be made by dissolving fruit juice, sugar and carbon dioxide in water.

A	fruit juice
B	sugar
C	carbon dioxide
D	water

Which of the above is **not** a solute?

A
B
C
D

KU	PS
1	

3. Distillation of crude oil produces several fractions.

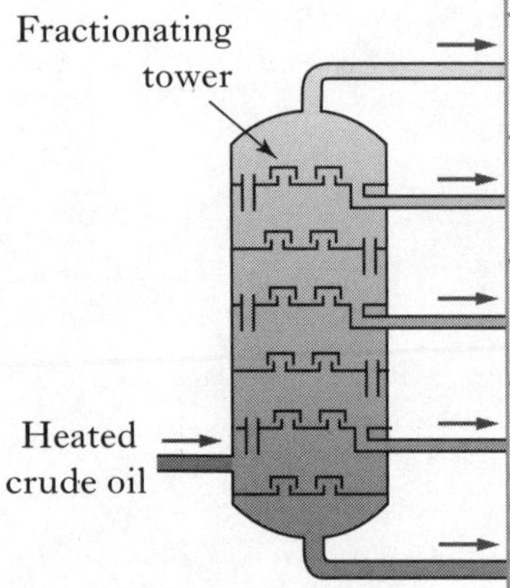

Fraction	Number of carbon atoms
A	$C_1 - C_4$
B	$C_5 - C_{10}$
C	$C_{10} - C_{16}$
D	$C_{15} - C_{28}$
E	$> C_{26}$

Fractionating tower

Heated crude oil

(a) Which fraction is used in petrol?

A
B
C
D
E

(b) Identify the fraction with the highest boiling point

A
B
C
D
E

KU   PS

1

(2)   1

4. The decomposition of hydrogen peroxide is catalysed using lumps of manganese dioxide.

$$2H_2O_2(\ell) \longrightarrow 2H_2O(\ell) + O_2(g)$$

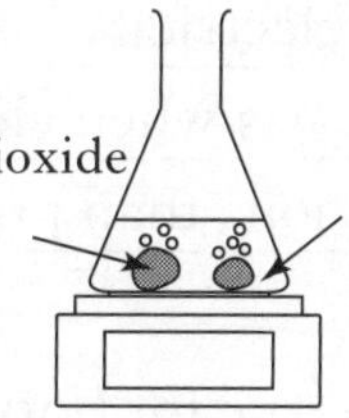

manganese dioxide lumps

hydrogen peroxide

A	Increasing the concentration of the hydrogen peroxide
B	Increasing the volume of the hydrogen peroxide
C	Using manganese dioxide powder
D	Heating the solution

(a) Which change would **not** increase the rate of the reaction?

| A |
| B |
| C |
| D |

(b) Which **two** changes would increase the volume of oxygen produced?

| A |
| B |
| C |
| D |

(3)

KU PS

1

2

5. The grid shows some statements which could be applied to a solution.

A	It reacts with copper.
B	It has a pH of less than 7.
C	It does not conduct electricity.
D	It produces chlorine gas when electrolysed.
E	It contains more H^+ ions than pure water.

Identify the **two** statements which are true for **both** dilute hydrochloric acid and dilute nitric acid.

A
B
C
D
E

KU PS

2

KU PS

6. Many compounds contain carbon, hydrogen and oxygen.

A
$$H-\overset{\overset{\displaystyle O}{\|}}{C}-O-H$$

B
$$H-\overset{\overset{\displaystyle H}{|}}{\underset{\underset{\displaystyle H}{|}}{C}}-\overset{\overset{\displaystyle O}{\|}}{C}-O-H$$

C
$$H-\overset{\overset{\displaystyle H}{|}}{\underset{\underset{\displaystyle H}{|}}{C}}-\overset{\overset{\displaystyle H}{|}}{\underset{\underset{\displaystyle H}{|}}{C}}-\overset{\overset{\displaystyle O}{\|}}{C}-H$$

D
$$H-\overset{\overset{\displaystyle H}{|}}{\underset{\underset{\displaystyle H}{|}}{C}}-\overset{\overset{\displaystyle H}{|}}{\underset{\underset{\displaystyle H}{|}}{C}}-\overset{\overset{\displaystyle H}{|}}{\underset{\underset{\displaystyle H}{|}}{C}}-O-H$$

E
$$H-\overset{\overset{\displaystyle H}{|}}{\underset{\underset{\displaystyle H}{|}}{C}}-\overset{\overset{\displaystyle O}{\|}}{C}-\overset{\overset{\displaystyle H}{|}}{\underset{\underset{\displaystyle H}{|}}{C}}-H$$

(a) Identify the **two** compounds with the same molecular formula.

A
B
C
D
E

(b) Identify the compound which has the general formula $C_nH_{2n+2}O$.

A
B
C
D
E

	KU	PS
		1
		1

(2)

7. The grid below shows pairs of chemicals.

A	B
$CuO + C$	$Na + H_2O$
C	D
$Cu + NaNO_3$	$C_5H_{12} + O_2$
E	F
$Mg + H_2SO_4$	$Ag + HCl$

Which **two** boxes contain pairs of chemicals that do **not** react together?

A	B
C	D
E	F

KU | PS

2

8. The voltage between a pair of metals can be measured when they are connected in a circuit through an electrolyte.

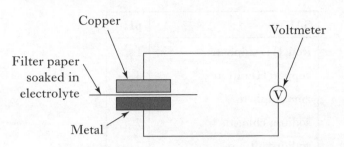

Metal	Voltage	Direction of electron flow through voltmeter
1	0·5 V	metal → copper
2	0·3 V	copper → metal
3	1·0 V	metal → copper
4	0·2 V	copper → metal

Identify the correct statements.

A	Metal 3 is the most reactive
B	Metal 1 is found uncombined in the ground
C	Metals 2 and 4 are the hardest to obtain from their compounds
D	Metal 2 is displaced from its salts by metal 3
E	Metals 1 and 3 give a higher voltage than any other pair of metals when connected in a cell

KU | PS

2

9. The pH of 1 mol/l solutions of some salts are shown below.

SALT	pH
iron(III) sulphate	1
copper(II) nitrate	3
zinc sulphate	3
sodium chloride	7
sodium nitrate	7
potassium sulphate	7
sodium carbonate	10
potassium carbonate	11

Identify the **two** statements which can be made about the salts in the table.

A	The salts of transition metals are acidic
B	The sulphates are acidic
C	The salts of sodium are neutral
D	Salts of group 1 metals are alkaline
E	The salts of carbonic acid are alkaline

```
A
B
C
D
E
```

2

10. The melting points and boiling points of some compounds are shown below.

compound	name	melting point (°C)	boiling point (°C)
A	ammonia	−78	−33
B	nitrogen dioxide	−11	21
C	sulphur dioxide	−73	−10
D	water	0	100

Which compound will be a liquid at −25°C?

A
B
C
D

KU	PS
	1

PART 2

A total of 40 marks is available in this part of the paper.

11. There are two common types of potassium atom; $^{39}_{19}K$ and $^{41}_{19}K$.

    (a) What name is used to describe the different types of potassium atom?

    _____

	1

    (b) Potassium has a relative atomic mass of 39·1.

    What can be said about the relative abundance of each type of potassium atom?

    _____

    _____

    _____

    _____

	1

    (c) Complete the table to show the number of protons, neutrons and electrons in the $^{39}_{19}K^+$ ion.

PARTICLE	NUMBER
proton	
neutrons	
electrons	

    (4)

2	

12. Alkynes are a homologous series of hydrocarbons which contain a carbon to carbon triple bond.

$$H—C\equiv C—H \qquad \text{ethyne}$$

$$H—C\equiv C—\overset{\displaystyle H}{\underset{\displaystyle H}{\overset{|}{\underset{|}{C}}}}—H \qquad \text{propyne}$$

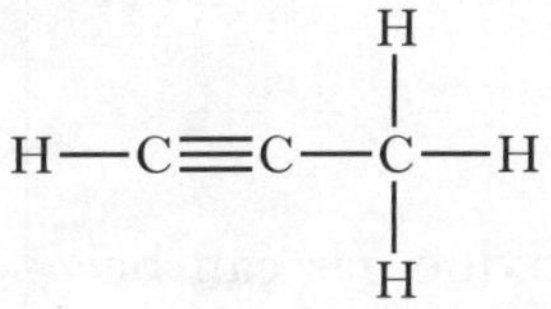

$$H—C\equiv C—\overset{\displaystyle H}{\underset{\displaystyle H}{\overset{|}{\underset{|}{C}}}}—\overset{\displaystyle H}{\underset{\displaystyle H}{\overset{|}{\underset{|}{C}}}}—H \qquad \text{butyne}$$

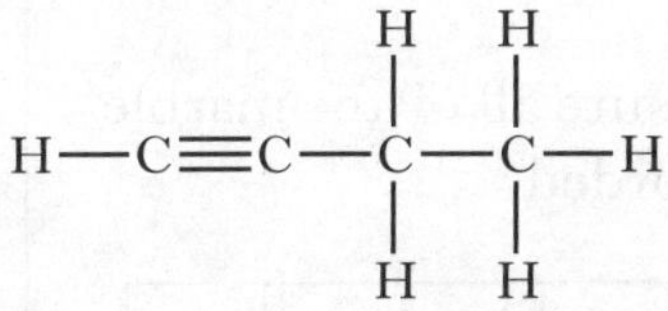

(a) What is the general formula of the alkynes?

_____

(b) What would be the products of burning an alkyne in a plentiful supply of air?

_____

(c) Write the molecular formula for the product of the complete reaction of propyne with hydrogen.

_____

(d) Draw the structural formula for an isomer of propyne which contains **one** carbon to carbon double bond per molecule.

(4)

KU	PS
1	
	1
	1
	1

13. Marble chips (calcium carbonate) react with hydrochloric acid producing carbon dioxide gas.

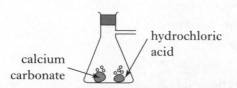

(a) Complete the diagram above to show how the carbon dioxide gas can be collected and the volume of gas measured.

(b) In an experiment 1 mol/l HCl was used in excess, to ensure all of the marble chips react, and the results in the table below were recorded.

Time (minutes)	0	10	20	30	40	50	60	70	80	90
Volume of gas (cm³)	0	22	38	50	59	66	73	78	80	80

Draw a line graph of the results.

Use appropriate scales to fill most of the graph paper.

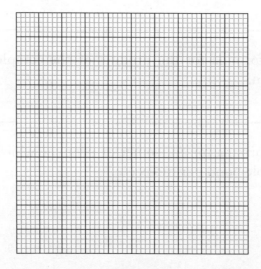

(c) Sketch on the graph the results you would expect if the experiment was repeated with 2 mol/l hydrochloric acid.

(5)

KU | PS

2

2

1

14. The enzyme zymase (found in yeast) is used to ferment alcohol from glucose. During the reaction carbon dioxide is also produced.

$$C_6H_{12}O_6(aq) \xrightarrow{\text{zymase}} 2C_2H_5OH(aq) + 2CO_2(g)$$

(a) What is meant by an enzyme?

_____

(b) The activity of the zymase was measured at different pHs.

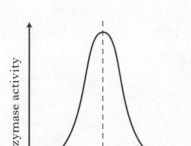

What effect does increasing the pH have on the activity of zymase?

_____

_____

(c) In some foods the glucose comes from the breakdown of starch.

What name is given to the **type** of reaction where starch is broken down to form glucose?

_____

(d) The diagram below shows how glucose can be fermented to produce alcohol.

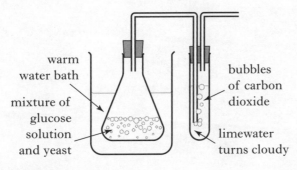

If the lime water had been replaced with Universal Indicator what colour change would be observed?

_____

(4)

KU | PS
1 |
 | 1
1 |
 | 1

15. Carbon tetrachloride is a covalent molecule with the formula CCl_4.

(*a*) Draw a diagram to show how the outer electrons of carbon and hydrogen form the covalent molecule CCl_4.

(*b*) Draw a diagram to show the **shape** of a molecule of tetrachloromethane.

(2)

	KU	PS
	1	
	1	

KU	PS

16. Many cans used for foodstuffs are made of iron.

		KU	PS

(a) If it comes into contact with water and oxygen an unprotected iron can will rust.

Name the **ion** formed, during rusting, when water and oxygen accept electrons.

_____

KU: 1

(b) The can contained salt water. What effect would this have on the rate of rusting when the can is opened?

_____

_____

PS: 1

(c) Food cans are commonly called 'tin cans' because they are coated in tin. The tin coating protects the iron can from rusting.

Why do tin cans rust **more** quickly, than uncoated cans, when scratched?

_____

_____

_____

KU: 1

(3)

17. The monomer vinyl chloride is use in the production of poly(vinylchloride).

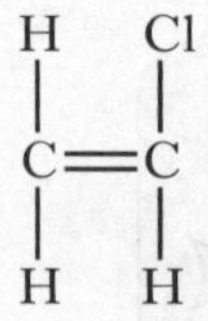

$$\begin{array}{ccc} H & & Cl \\ | & & | \\ C & = & C \\ | & & | \\ H & & H \end{array}$$

(a) Draw a section of the poly(vinylchloride) polymer, showing 3 monomer units joined together.

(b) Name a toxic gas produced when poly(vinylchloride) burns.

_____

(2)

KU	PS
1	
1	
KU	PS

18. Ammonia is made from nitrogen and hydrogen in the Haber Process.

nitrogen and hydrogen $\rightleftharpoons$ ammonia

(a) Explain why **all** the nitrogen and hydrogen is **not** converted into ammonia in this process.

_____

_____

_____

(b) The process is carried out at approximately 450°C.

Why is the process not carried out at higher temperatures?

(c) The production of ammonia in the Haber Process is exothermic.

Why would this be an advantage in the production of ammonia?

_____

_____

_____

(3)

KU	PS
1	
1	
	1

19. The colours of some ionic solutions are shown in the table below.

Ionic solution	Colour
nickel(II) chloride	green
nickel(II) iodide	green
sodium chloride	colourless
sodium dichromate	orange

(a) Using the table give the colour of the sodium ion.

_____

(b) Write the **ionic** formula for sodium dichromate.

_____

(c) The following experiment was used to investigate the colour of the ions in cobalt (II) sulphate.

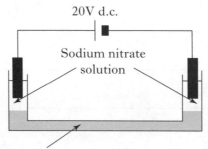

20V d.c.

Sodium nitrate
solution

Gel containing cobalt(II) sulphate solution

The following observations were recorded.

pink colour appears at the negative electrode
positive electrode remains colourless

(i) What is the colour of the cobalt(II) ion?

_____

(ii) What was the purpose of the electrolyte, sodium nitrate?

_____

(iii) Why would barium nitrate have been unsuitable as the electrolyte?

You may wish to use the data booklet to help you.

_____

_____

(5)

KU | PS

1

1

1

1

1

20. Sodium hydroxide solution was titrated with sulphuric acid as shown below.

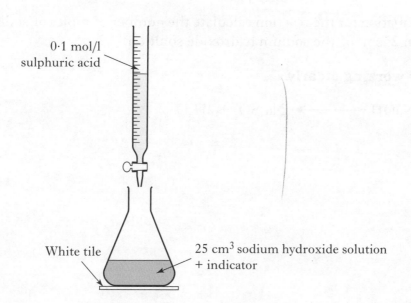

0·1 mol/l sulphuric acid

White tile

25 cm³ sodium hydroxide solution + indicator

The following results were obtained

Titration	Initial volume (cm³)	Final volume (cm³)	Volume of sulphuric acid added (cm³)
1	0·6	22·5	21·9
2	0·2	21·7	21·5
3	0·4	21·7	21·3

Average volume of sulphuric acid used = 21·4cm³

(a) In the titration how would it be possible to tell when all of the sodium hydroxide had been neutralised?

_____

_____

1

(b) Why was the result of the first titration ignored when calculating the average volume of sulphuric acid used?

_____

_____

1

(c) Calculate the number of moles of sulphuric acid present in the average volume used.

Show your working clearly.

1

_____mol

20. (Continued)

(*d*) Given the equation for the reaction calculate the number of moles of sodium hydroxide in 25cm^3 of the sodium hydroxide solution.

Show your working clearly.

$$H_2SO_4 + 2NaOH \longrightarrow Na_2SO_4 + 2H_2O$$

_____ mol

(4)

	KU	PS
	1	

21. In a blast furnace iron ore reacts with carbon monoxide, forming molten iron metal

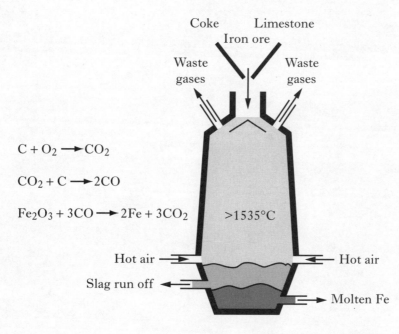

$$C + O_2 \longrightarrow CO_2$$

$$CO_2 + C \longrightarrow 2CO$$

$$Fe_2O_3 + 3CO \longrightarrow 2Fe + 3CO_2$$

(a) Name the type of reaction taking place when a metal is extracted from its ore.

_____

(b) Why must the temperature in the blast furnace be kept above 1535°C?

You may wish to use the data booklet to help you.

_____

_____

(c) Aluminium has to be extracted from its ore by electrolysis.

(i) Why can aluminium not be extracted from its ore by heating with carbon monoxide?

_____

_____

(ii) If aluminum chloride were electrolysed what would be formed at the positive electrode?

_____

_____

(4)

KU	PS
1	
	1
1	
	1

Practice Exam B

Chemistry   Standard Grade: Credit

Practice Papers	Time allowed:	**Exam B**
For SQA Exams	1 hour 30 minutes	**Credit Level**

Fill in these boxes:

Name of center

Town

Forename(s)

Surname

Try to answer all of the questions in the time allowed.

Write your answers in the spaces provided, including all of your working.

Full marks will only be awarded where your answer includes any relevant working.

You will find necessary data in the Standard Grade and Intermediate 2 SQA Data Booklet.

You must do your rough work in this exam book – but it must be clearly crossed out.

Leckie×Leckie
Scotland's leading educational publishers

1. The Periodic Table is a list of the elements.

Six common elements are listed in the grid.

A	B	C
lithium	oxygen	phosphorus
D	E	F
potassium	chlorine	calcium

(a) Identify the **two** elements with similar chemical properties.

A	B	C
D	E	F

(b) Identify the element which can form ions with the same electron arrangement as neon.

A	B	C
D	E	F

(c) Identify the two elements which form an ionic compound with the formula of the type XY_2, where **X** is the metal.

A	B	C
D	E	F

(3)

KU | PS

1

1

1

2. The following grid shows several experiments with acids and metals.

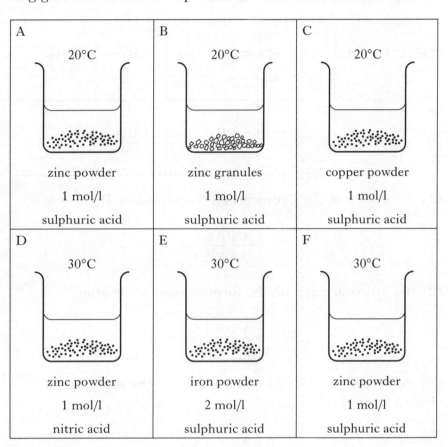

A 20°C zinc powder 1 mol/l sulphuric acid	**B** 20°C zinc granules 1 mol/l sulphuric acid	**C** 20°C copper powder 1 mol/l sulphuric acid
D 30°C zinc powder 1 mol/l nitric acid	**E** 30°C iron powder 2 mol/l sulphuric acid	**F** 30°C zinc powder 1 mol/l sulphuric acid

(a) Identify the **two** experiments which could be compared to show the effect of temperature on reaction rate.

A	B	C
D	E	F

(b) Identify the experiment in which no reaction takes place.

A	B	C
D	E	F

KU | PS

1

1

(2)

3. The following grid contains the structural formula of some hydrocarbons.

A	B	C
$CH_3-CH_2-CH_2-CH_3$	$CH_3-CH=CH_2$	$CH_3-\overset{\displaystyle |}{\underset{\displaystyle CH_3}{C}}=CH_2$
D	E	F
H_2C-CH_2 $\diagdown \diagup$ CH_2	$CH_3-CH_2-CH_3$	$CH_2=CH_2$

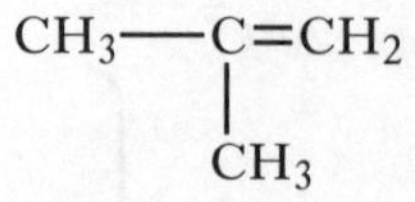

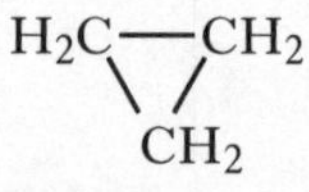

(a) Identify the isomer of the hydrocarbon shown in box **D**.

A	B	C
D	E	F

(b) Identify the hydrocarbon with the formula mass of 44 amu.

A	B	C
D	E	F

(c) Identify the **two** hydrocarbons which belong to the same homologous series as C_5H_{12}.

A	B	C
D	E	F

(3)

KU: 1

1

1

4. A voltage can be produced when two different metals are joined in a cell.

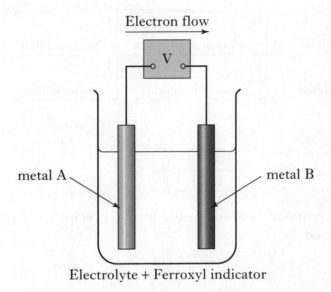

Electron flow

metal A

metal B

Electrolyte + Ferroxyl indicator

	metal A	metal B
A	magnesium	iron
B	iron	copper
C	copper	zinc
D	copper	magnesium
E	aluminium	zinc

(*a*) Which pair of metals would give a flow of electrons in the same direction as in the diagram above **and** produce a blue colour around electrode **A**?

A
B
C
D
E

(*b*) Which pair of metals would give the largest voltage?
You may wish to use the data booklet to help you.

A
B
C
D
E

(2)

KU | PS

1

1

5. The following grid contains some soluble compounds.

A	B	C
sodium bromide	ammonium chloride	barium iodide
D	E	F
lithium carbonate	potassium chloride	sodium nitrate

(a) Identify the base.

A	B	C
D	E	F

(b) Identify the **two** compounds which would form a precipitate if their solutions were mixed.

A	B	C
D	E	F

(2)

KU   PS

1

1

6. The table gives information about some gaseous elements at room temperature.

Substance	Relative formula mass	Density of gas relative to hydrogen	Boiling point (°C)
neon	20	10	−249
nitrogen	28	13	−210
fluorine	38	17	−220
argon	40	18	−189
chlorine	71	32	−101

Identify the **two** statements which can be made from the information in the table

A	The boiling point of a gas depends on the density.
B	The diatomic gases have greater densities than the monoatomic gases.
C	The density of a gas increases with an increase in relative formula mass.
D	The boiling point of a gas does **not** depend on the relative formula mass.

A
B
C
D

KU | PS

2

7. The grid contains the formulae of some oxides.

A	B	C
CO	H_2O	Na_2O
D	E	F
NO_2	SO_2	SiO_2

(a) Identify the oxide produced by the sparking of air.

A	B	C
D	E	F

(b) Identify the gas whose concentration is decreased when the air to fuel ratio is increased.

A	B	C
D	E	F

(2)

KU	PS
	1
	1

8. Iron fishing boats need to be protected from rusting.
Identify the **two** correct statements.

A	Salt water speeds up rusting.
B	Iron rusts faster when coated in zinc.
C	Copper gives sacrificial protection to the iron.
D	The rusting of iron is an example of oxidation.
E	Ferroxyl indicator turns pink in the presence of Fe^{2+}.

A
B
C
D
E

2

9. The grid contains some carbohydrates.

A	fructose
B	glucose
C	maltose
D	starch
E	sucrose

(a) Lactose is a disaccharide found in milk.
Identify the two isomers of lactose.

A
B
C
D
E

1

(b) Identify the carbohydrate which would give **no** reaction with **both** iodine and Benedict's tests?

A
B
C
D
E

1

(2)

KU	PS

PART 2

A total of 40 marks is available in this part of the paper.

10. A sample of nitrogen was found to contain two different types of atom; $^{14}_{7}N$ and $^{15}_{7}N$.

   (a) (i) What term is used to describe these different types of nitrogen atom?

   _____

   (ii) The average atomic mass of this sample of nitrogen was 14·05. What is the mass number of the most common type of atom in this sample?

   _____

   (iii) Complete the table showing the number of protons and neutrons in each type of atom.

Type of atom	Number of protons	Number of neutrons
$^{14}_{7}N$		
$^{15}_{7}N$		

   (b) In an ammonia molecule (NH_3), a nitrogen atom forms bonds with hydrogen atoms.
   Draw a diagram to show the **shape** of an ammonia molecule.

(4)

	KU	PS
(a)(i)	1	
(a)(ii)		1
(a)(iii)	1	
(b)	1	

11. Ethanol is an alcohol which can be produced in the following experiment.

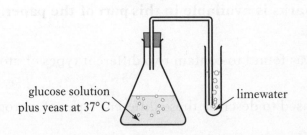

glucose solution
plus yeast at 37°C

limewater

(a) (i) What name is given to the type of reaction where ethanol is formed from glucose in the presence of yeast?

    1

(ii) What would happen to the rate of reaction if the temperature were increased from 37°C to 60°C?

    1

(b) Alcohols can be made in industry from alkenes as shown below.

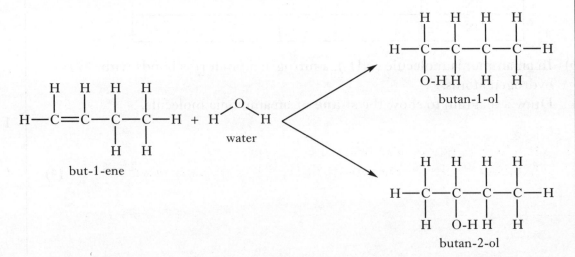

but-1-ene

water

butan-1-ol

butan-2-ol

(i) What name is given to the type of reaction taking place above?

    1

(ii) Butan-1-ol and butan-2-ol have different boiling points. What process could be used to separate these alcohols?

    1

(4)

12. Polystyrene is used in cups and ceiling tiles.
Part of a polystyrene molecule is shown below.

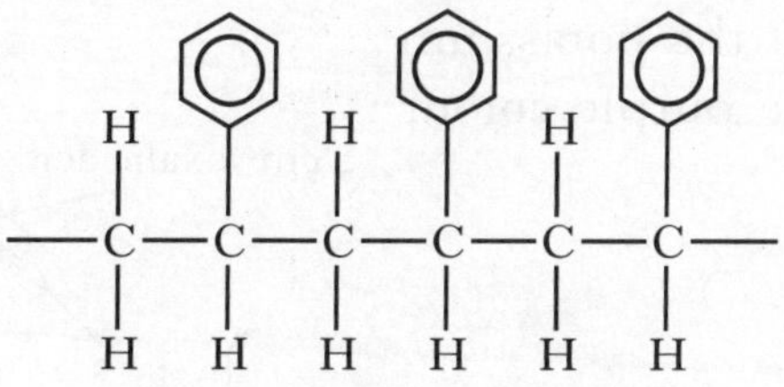

Key: $\hexagon$ = C_6H_5

(a) Draw the structural formula for the monomer used to make the polystyrene.

| | 1 | |

(b) When heated, polystyrene begins to melt.
What name is given to the type of plastic which melts on heating?

_____

| | 1 | |

(c) What poisonous gas is likely to be formed if polystyrene catches fire?

| | 1 | |

_____

(3)

KU	PS

13. The effect of concentration on the rate of a reaction was investigated using the following experiment.

The oxalic acid reacts with potassium permanganate and when all the potassium permanganate is reacted the purple colour disappears.

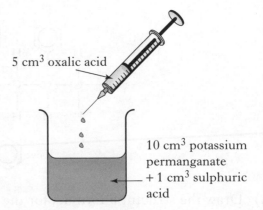

5 cm³ oxalic acid

10 cm³ potassium permanganate
+ 1 cm³ sulphuric acid

The results of an investigation are shown below

Concentration of oxalic acid (mol/l)	Time for purple colour to disappear (s)
1·0	120
1·5	88
2·0	56
2·5	24

(a) (i) Draw a line graph of the results.

Use appropriate scales to fill most of the graph paper.

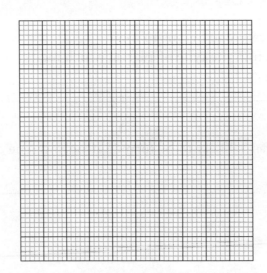

(ii) Use your graph to estimate the length of time for the reaction if 0·5 mol/l oxalic acid had been used.

_____

(b) Describe the relationship between concentration and the **speed** of the reaction.

_____

_____

(4)

KU | PS

2

1

1

14. Ammonia gas can be produced by heating ammonium sulphate with sodium hydroxide.

The equation for this reaction is:

$$NaOH + (NH_4)_2SO_4 \longrightarrow Na_2SO_4 + NH_3 + H_2O$$

(*a*) Balance the above equation

(*b*) What effect would the ammonia produced have on moist pH paper.

(2)

KU	PS
1	
1	

15. Amines are a family of compounds which contain the group

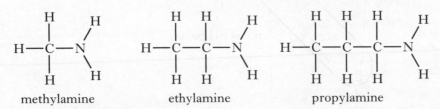

The **full** structural formula of the first three amines are shown.

| methylamine | ethylamine | propylamine |

(a) Draw the **full** structural formula for the amine containing 4 carbon atoms.

1

(b) The table gives information on the boiling point of some amines

Amine	Boiling point/°C
ethylamine	17
propylamine	49
butylamine	77
pentylamine	103

(i) Using this information, make a general statement linking the boiling point to the number of carbon atoms.

1

(ii) Predict the boiling point of hexylamine.

1

_____°C

(3)

16. Hydrochloric acid was neutralised by adding solid magnesium carbonate until some solid remained.

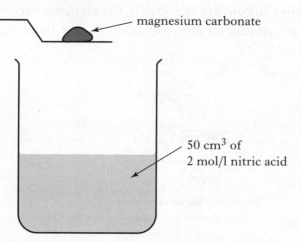

magnesium carbonate

50 cm³ of
2 mol/l nitric acid

(a) Calculate the number of moles of dilute nitric acid in the beaker.

_____ mol

(b) The equation for the reaction is

$$MgCO_3(s) + 2HNO_3(aq) \longrightarrow Mg(NO_3)_2(aq) + H_2O(l) + CO_2(g)$$

(i) Using the answer to part (a) calculate the number of moles of magnesium carbonate needed to neutralise the dilute nitric acid.

_____ mol

(ii) Using the answer to part (b) (i), calculate the **mass** of magnesium carbonate ($MgCO_3$) required to neutralise the acid.

_____ g

(c) What would have been observed in the experiment to indicate that this reaction was happening?

_____

(d) Why would magnesium carbonate be added until some solid remained?

_____

(5)

KU	PS
1	
1	
1	
	1
	1

17. Plants need nitrogen to grow. The main source of nitrogen is the air, but it must first be 'fixed' into nitrogen compounds which the plants can use. Leguminose plants like peas and beans can convert nitrogen in the air into nitrogen compounds. Man-made fertilisers are produced after nitrogen is first fixed industrially into ammonia.

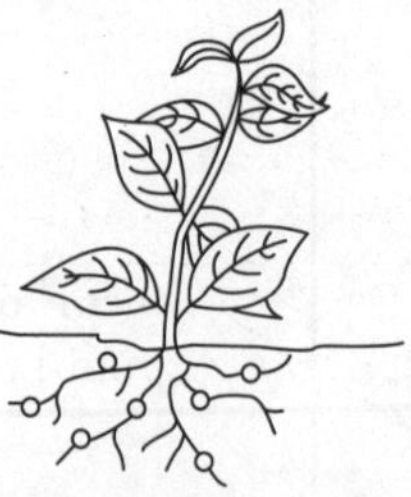

Nitrifying bacteria in root
nodules do the job!

(a) Name the **industrial** process used to fix nitrogen from the air.

_____

(b) Apart from saving money, what is the advantage of using nitrogen-fixing bacteria over industrial fertilisers?

_____

(2)

KU	PS
1	
	1

18. The table contains information on some metal ores

Ore	Formula
bauxite	Al_2O_3
cinnabar	HgS
galena	PbS
haematite	Fe_2O_3
magnesite	$MgCO_3$

(a) Give the chemical name for galena.

_____

(b) Name the salt formed when bauxite reacts with hydrochloric acid.

_____

(c) Iron can be extracted from its ore by heating with carbon monoxide.

Calculate the mass of iron which could be produced from 16 tons of haematite (Fe_2O_3) in the following reaction.

Show your working clearly.

$$Fe_2O_3 + 3CO \longrightarrow 2Fe + 3CO_2$$

(d) Name a metal which can be extracted from its ore by heat alone.

_____

(5)

KU	PS
	1
	1
2	
1	

19. The reaction between iodide ions with bromine solution can be used to form a cell. The iodide ions are oxidised, with the ion electron equation being:

$$2I^-(aq) + 2e^- \longrightarrow I_2(aq)$$

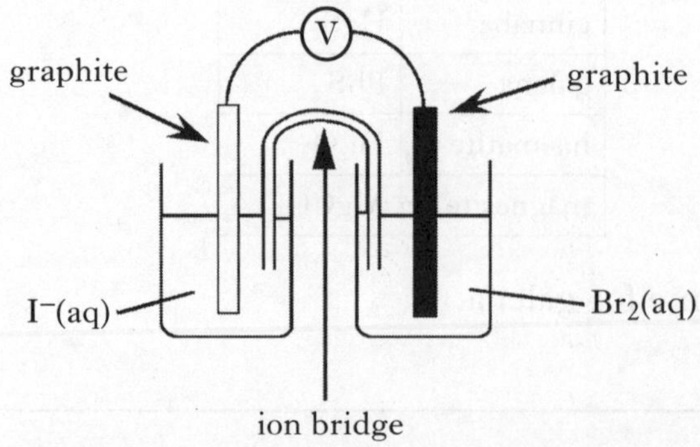

(a) **On the diagram**, clearly mark the path and direction of electron flow.

(b) (i) Potassium nitrate is used as the electrolyte. What is the purpose of the electrolyte?

_____

_____

(ii) Suggest why silver nitrate can**not** be used as the electrolyte. You may wish to use the data booklet to help you.

_____

_____

(c) In the reaction, the bromine solution is reduced. Write the ion-electron equation for this reaction.

(4)

	KU	PS

20. An experiment was carried out using three chemicals labelled **A, B** and **C.**

The chemicals were:

sucrose solution, dilute nitric acid and nickel chloride solution.

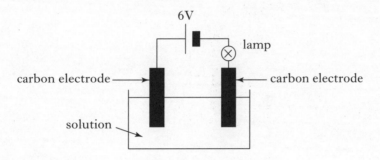

The results obtained were;

solution	Did the lamp light?	Observations at electrodes
A	yes	bubbles formed at negative electrode
B	yes	solid formed at negative electrode
C	no	no reaction

(a) When electricity was passed through solutions A and B, they were broken up.

What term is used to describe this process?

_____

(b) (i) Identify chemical **A**

_____

(ii) Describe what would be **seen** at the positive electrode when electricity was passed through solution **B.**

_____

_____

(iii) What type of bonding is present in **C**?

_____

(4)

Practice Exam C

Chemistry   Standard Grade: Credit

Practice Papers For SQA Exams	Time allowed: 1 hour 30 minutes	Exam C Credit Level

Fill in these boxes:

Name of center

Town

Forename(s)

Surname

Try to answer all of the questions in the time allowed.

Write your answers in the spaces provided, including all of your working.

Full marks will only be awarded where your answer includes any relevant working.

You will find necessary data in the Standard Grade and Intermediate 2 SQA Data Booklet.

You must do your rough work in this exam book – but it must be clearly crossed out.

1. The Periodic Table is a list of the elements.

Six common elements are listed in the grid.

A	B	C
aluminium	bromine	chlorine
D	E	F
lithium	oxygen	potassium

(a) Identify the **two** elements which can form ions with the same electron arrangement as argon.

A	B	C
D	E	F

(b) Identify the elements which belong to the Halogen family

A	B	C
D	E	F

(c) Identify the two elements which could react to form a compound with the formula X_2Y_3.

A	B	C
D	E	F

(3)

KU   PS

1

1

1

2. The grid below contains compounds formed from two elements.

A	B	C
$NiCl_2$	FeO	Na_2O
D	E	F
NaCl	SO_2	SiO_2

(*a*) Identify the **two** covalent compounds.

A	B	C
D	E	F

1

(*b*) Identify the compound which will produce an alkaline solution when added to water.

A	B	C
D	E	F

1

(2)

KU	PS

			KU	PS

3. Magnesium was added to sulphuric acid in a classroom investigation into rates of reaction.

Four experiments were carried out under different conditions, that would each ensure that all of the magnesium reacted.

A graph of the results of each experiment is shown below.

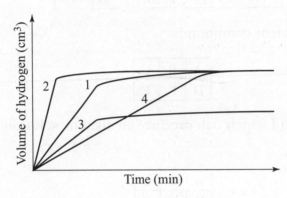

Graph 1 was obtained using:

1g magnesium powder with 1 mol/l sulphuric acid at 20°C.

Identify the correct statements below.

A	Experiment 2 would give this graph using 1g magnesium powder and 0·5 mol/l acid at 20°C.
B	Experiment 3 would give this graph using 1g magnesium powder and 1 mol/l acid at 10°C.
C	Experiment 3 would give this graph using 0·5g magnesium powder and 1 mol/l acid at 20°C.
D	Experiment 4 would give this graph using 1g magnesium powder and 1 mol/l acid at 30°C.
E	Experiment 4 would give this graph using 1g magnesium ribbon and 1 mol/l acid at 20°C.

2

4. If water is added to 1 mol/l sulphuric acid which of the following statements is correct?

A	The pH decreases
B	The acid is neutralised.
C	The concentration of H^+(aq) ions decreases.
D	The speed of the acids reaction with zinc decreases.
E	The number of sulphate ions in the solution decreases.
F	The volume of alkali needed to neutralise the acid decreases.

A
B
C
D
E
F

KU PS

2

5. The results of some experiments into the reactions of metals and their compounds are listed below.

The metals used were copper, iron, magnesium, nickel, zinc and an unknown metal **X**.

A	X displaces zinc from zinc sulphate
B	X is more readily oxidised than nickel.
C	X oxide is more stable than copper oxide.
D	X reacts more quickly than iron with acid.
E	Compounds of X are more readily reduced than compounds of magnesium.

The following order of reactivity was produced.

Magnesium, zinc, iron, **X**, nickel, copper

← **Decreasing activity** →

Identify the two observations which can be used to show that **X** has been **incorrectly** placed in the order of reactivity.

A
B
C
D
E

2

6. Some salts can be formed by precipitation.

A	B
barium sulphate	lithium iodide
C	D
potassium carbonate	zinc chloride

(a) Identify the salt which can be formed by precipitation.

You may wish to use the data booklet to help you.

A	B
C	D

(b) Identify the two soluble salts which will form a precipitate when their solutions are mixed.

You may wish to use the data booklet to help you.

A	B	C
D	E	F

(2)

KU	PS
	1
	1

7. The properties of the following substances are related to their bonding.

Substance	Melting point (°C)	Boiling point (°C)	Conducts electricity as a solid	Conducts electricity as a liquid
A	68	671	yes	yes
B	770	1680	no	yes
C	−9	21	no	no
D	−154	−101	no	no
E	−40	71	no	no
F	1610	2230	no	no

(a) Identify the substance which is a liquid at 25°C

A
B
C
D
E
F

(b) Identify the substance with ionic bonding.

A
B
C
D
E
F

(c) Identify the substance which is a covalent network.

A
B
C
D
E
F

(3)

KU PS

1

1

1

KU	PS

8. Copper(II) sulphate solution can react with potassium iodide solution in a redox reaction.

$$2CuSO_4 + 4KI \longrightarrow 2CuI + I_2 + 2K_2SO_4$$

The grid shows the ions present during the reaction.

A	Cu^{2+}
B	SO_4^{2-}
C	K^+
D	I^-
E	Cu^+

(*a*) Identify the ion which has been oxidised.

You may wish to use the data book to help you.

A
B
C
D
E

PS: 1

(*b*) Identify the **two** spectator ions in this reaction.

A
B
C
D
E

KU: 1

(2)

9. The steel hulls of ships can be protected from rusting by attaching bars of zinc.

Identify the **two** correct statements below.

A	Copper could stop corrosion in the same manner as zinc.
B	Electrons flow from the iron to the zinc.
C	The iron would corrode faster than the zinc.
D	The zinc provides sacrificial protection.
E	The zinc is oxidised.

| A |
| B |
| C |
| D |
| E |

(2)

KU	PS
2	

PART 2

A total of 40 marks is available in this part of the paper.

	KU	PS

10. Although bromine has a relative atomic mass of 80, an atom of bromine with a mass of 80 does not exist.

Bromine is found as two isotopes: $^{79}_{35}Br$ and $^{81}_{35}Br$

(a) What is meant by the term 'isotope'?

_____

_____

(b) If the relative atomic mass of bromine is 80 what can be said about the relative amounts of each isotope?

_____

_____

(c) Using only the outer electrons, show how two bromine atoms form a covalent bond.

_____

_____

(d) Explain how the atoms in a bromine molecule are held together by a covalent bond.

(You may find it helpful to draw a diagram.)

_____

_____

(e) As a result of having two isotopes bromine can form three molecules each with a different formula mass.

What are the three possible masses of a Br_2 molecule?

_____

(5)

11. Crude oil is separated by fractional distillation.

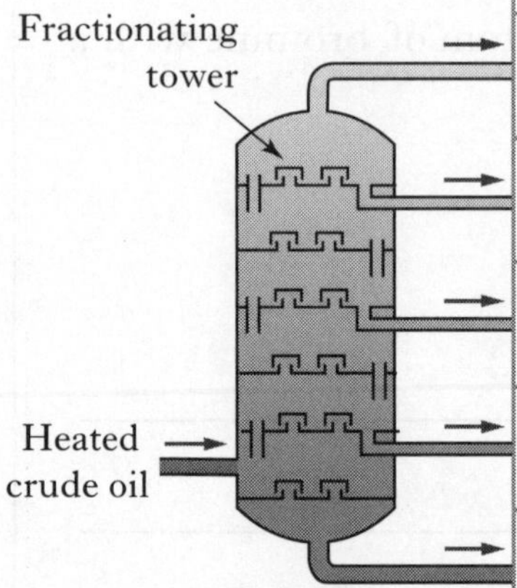

	KU	PS

Fractionating tower

Heated crude oil

Fraction	Boiling range (°C)	Number of carbon atoms per molecule
Refinery gas	<20	1–4
Naphtha	20–130	5–12
Kerosene	130–240	11–16
Gas oil	240–350	15–25
Residue	>350	>25

(a) In which fraction will octane be found?

_____   1

(b) Why does the gas oil fraction have a higher boiling range than the naphtha fraction?   1

_____

_____

(c) Gas oil fractions are often cracked.

(i) Why are these fractions cracked?   1

_____

_____

(ii) Catalysts can be used to speed up cracking, but what other advantage to they give?   1

_____

_____

(4)

	KU	PS

12. Radioactive iodine ($^{131}_{53}$I) was used in medicine. It was injected into patients to investigate disease of the thyroid gland.

The radioactivity decreases over time and this was monitored.

The following data was recorded for the radioactivity of $^{131}_{53}$I in counts per minute (cpm)

Time (days)	0	5	8	12	16	24	32
Radioactivity (cpm)	40	28	20	15	10	5	2·5

(a) Draw a line graph of the results

Use appropriate scales to fill most of the graph paper

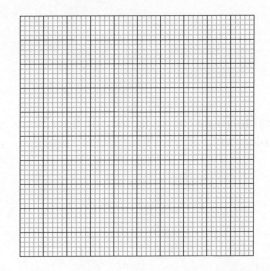

2

(b) Half-life is the time taken for the radioactivity of an isotope to halve.

This never changes for an isotope.

Use the information given to calculate the half-life of $^{131}_{53}$I.

1

(c) Recently $^{132}_{53}$I has been used to investigate thyroid disease, as it has a shorter half life than $^{131}_{53}$I.

Why is this an advantage?

1

(d) Complete the following table for an atom of $^{131}_{53}$I.

Particle	Number
proton	
neutron	

(5) 1

13. But-2-ene is shown below

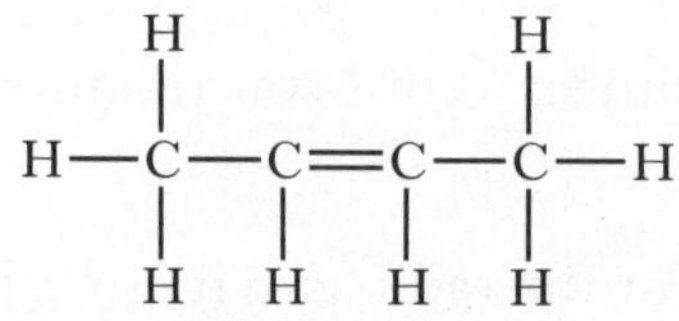

$$H-\overset{\overset{\displaystyle H}{|}}{\underset{\underset{\displaystyle H}{|}}{C}}-\overset{\overset{\displaystyle }{}}{\underset{\underset{\displaystyle H}{|}}{C}}=\overset{}{\underset{\underset{\displaystyle H}{|}}{C}}-\overset{\overset{\displaystyle H}{|}}{\underset{\underset{\displaystyle H}{|}}{C}}-H$$

	KU	PS

(a) But-2-ene quickly decolourises bromine solution, Br_2(aq).

Draw the **full** structural formula for the molecule produced in this reaction.

1

(b) Draw the **full** structural formula for an isomer of but-2-ene which does **not** decolourise bromine solution.

1

(c) But-2-ene can be used to make the polymer poly(butene).

Draw a section of the poly(butene) polymer, showing 3 monomer units joined together.

1

(3)

	KU	PS

14. A commercial house plant food contains iron (II) sulphate, ammonium phosphate and potassium nitrate.

		KU	PS

(a) Write the formula for iron(II)sulphate.

(b) Calculate the percentage, by mass, of nitrogen in ammonium phosphate $(NH_4)_3PO_4$.

(c) Ammonia for making fertilisers is produced in the Haber process.

$$N_2 + 3H_2 \rightleftharpoons 2NH_3$$

Different conditions give different percentage production of ammonia

Percentage NH_3 produced (%)

		Pressure (atm)		
		25	100	500
	100	91·7%	96·7%	99·4%
Temperature (°C)	300	27·4%	52·5%	79·7%
	500	2·9%	10·6%	31·9%

(i) Why is it not possible to turn all of the nitrogen and hydrogen into ammonia?

_____

_____

(ii) What effect does pressure have on the yield of ammonia?

_____

_____

(iii) Explain why the Haber process is carried out at 500°C even though a higher percentage of ammonia is produced at lower temperatures.

_____

_____

(6)

KU column marks: 1, 2, 1

PS column marks: 1, 1

15. Many metals form ores, for example: sodium carbonate, aluminium oxide and copper sulphide. An experiment was carried out to show what an ore was made of.

First a sample of powdered ore was heated as shown below.

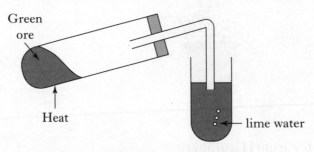

Results   Green ore turned black

Lime water turned chalky

(a) Name the **ion**, which the lime water turning chalky indicates is present in the ore.

(c) After heating, a black powder remained. This was heated with sulphuric acid, forming a blue solution.

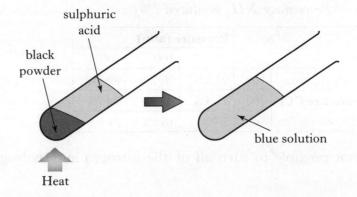

Being blue suggests that the ore may contain copper.

Describe an experiment, and the results you would expect, that could be carried out on the blue solution to show that it contained copper.

(*You may wish to draw a diagram.*)

(3)

KU	PS
	1
	2

16. The concentration of a sodium hydroxide solution can be determined by titration with sulphuric acid.

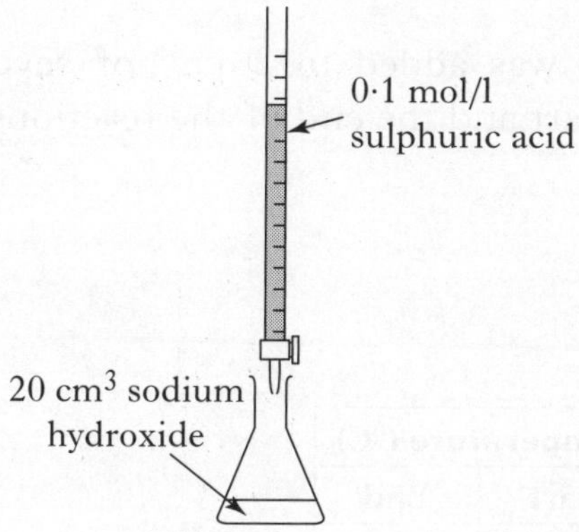

0·1 mol/l
sulphuric acid

20 cm³ sodium
hydroxide

The sodium hydroxide solution was neutralised by 20 cm³ of sulphuric acid.

(a) What would need to be added to the flask to show that all the sodium hydroxide had been neutralised?

_____

_____

(b) The equation for the reaction is:

$$H_2SO_4 + 2NaOH \longrightarrow Na_2SO_4 + 2H_2O$$

Use the result of the titration to calculate in moles per litre the concentration of the sodium hydroxide.

Show your working clearly

_____ mol/l

(3)

KU	PS
	1
2	

17. An experiment was carried out to investigate temperature changes during displacement reactions.

Excess aluminium powder was added to 20 cm³ of several solutions and the temperature noted at the start and the end of the reactions.

Solution	Temperature (°C)	
	Start	End
copper (II) nitrate	20	61
nickel (II) nitrate	20	48
iron (II) nitrate	20	40
zinc (II) nitrate	20	31

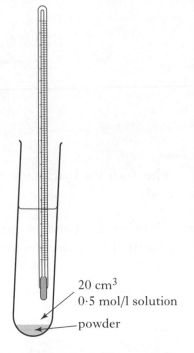

20 cm³
0·5 mol/l solution
powder

(a) What is the relationship between temperature change and the reactivity of the metals?

(You may wish to use the data booklet to help you)

_____

_____

(b) What end temperature would you expect if aluminium had been added to silver nitrate start temperature 20°C?

_____°C

(c) Name two ways in which the above investigation was fair.

_____

_____

(d) When zinc is added to copper (II) sulphate solution, copper metal is formed. Why is this an example of a reduction reaction?

_____

_____

(4)

KU   PS

1

1

1

1

18. Marathon runners will eat foods high in starch the night before a race

But during the race they will use drinks containing glucose.

(a) Why do foods containing glucose give us energy faster than starch?

_____

_____

(b) Glucose molecules can be joined together, to form the polymer starch, by removing water.

What name is given to this type of polymerization?

_____

(c) What has to happen to the starch, in our bodies, before we can use it to get energy.

_____

_____

(d) A sample of glucose was burned and the products tested.

glucose →

water condensing

ice + water

lime water turns chalky

to suction pump

This experiment indicated that water and carbon dioxide are produced.

What does this indicate about the elements present in glucose?

_____

_____

(4)

KU	PS
	1
1	
1	
1	

19. Aldehydes and ketones are families of compounds which both contain the carbonyl group C=O.

(a) What is the difference in structure between aldehydes and ketones?

_____

_____

(b) Tollens' reagent is a test chemical which contains silver ions (Ag^+).

Substances which react with Tollens' reagent, reduce the silver ions into silver atoms giving a 'silver mirror'.

$$Ag^+ + e^- \longrightarrow Ag$$

The table shows the results of testing the aldehydes and ketones above with Tollens' reagent.

Substance	Result with Tollens' reagent
propanal	silver mirror formed
propanone	No reaction
butanal	silver mirror formed
butanone	No reaction

(i) Explain why these results tell us that aldehydes can be oxidised but ketones can**not** be oxidised.

_____

_____

(ii) Explain why although aldehydes and ketones have the same General Formula ($C_nH_{2n}O$) they are **not** members of the same homologous series.

_____

_____

(3)

Practice Exam D

Chemistry

Standard Grade: Credit

Practice Papers
For SQA Exams

Time allowed:
1 hour 30 minutes

Exam D
Credit Level

Fill in these boxes:

Name of center

Town

Forename(s)

Surname

Try to answer all of the questions in the time allowed.

Write your answers in the spaces provided, including all of your working.

Full marks will only be awarded where your answer includes any relevant working.

You will find necessary data in the Standard Grade and Intermediate 2 SQA Data Booklet.

You must do your rough work in this exam book – but it must be clearly crossed out.

1. Different numbers are used in describing the structure of an atom.

A	The number of protons.
B	The number of neutrons.
C	The number of electrons.
D	The number of electrons in the outer energy level.

(a) Identify the two boxes which will be the same in a neutral atom.

A
B
C
D
E

1

(b) Which two boxes are added to give the Mass Number of an atom?

A
B
C
D
E

1

(c) Identify the two numbers which are the same for fluoride ions (F^-) and sodium ions (Na^+).

A
B
C
D
E

2

(4)

2. The grid gives the names of some hydrocarbons.

A	B	C
hexene	cyclohexane	ethene
D	E	F
propane	cyclobutane	heptane

(a) Identify the **two** unsaturated hydrocarbons.

A	B	C
D	E	F

(b) Which **two** hydrocarbons have the same molecular formula?

A	B	C
D	E	F

(c) Identify the **two** which could be produced by the cracking of pentane?

A	B	C
D	E	F

(3)

KU	PS
1	
	1
	1

3. Electricity is passed through a solution of nickel (II) sulphate

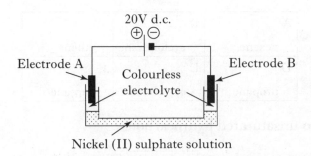

The nickel(II) sulphate solution contains green nickel ions and colourless sulphate ions.

Identify the two correct statements.

A	Nickel forms at electrode A.
B	Sulphate ions move towards electrode B.
C	A green colour moves towards electrode B.
D	The electrolyte around electrode A remains colourless.
E	Electrons move through the solution from electrode A to electrode B.

KU PS

2

(2)

4. The grid contains statements which can be applied to solutions.

A	It has pH less than 7.
B	It reacts with aluminium.
C	It is a good conductor of electricity.
D	It produces chlorine gas when electrolysed.
E	The concentration of H^+(aq) ions is equal to the concentration of hydroxide ions OH^-(aq).

(*a*) Identify the statement which can be applied to water **and** potassium chloride solution.

```
A
B
C
D
E
```

(*b*) Identify the **two** statements which can be applied to hydrochloric acid but **not** potassium chloride solution.

```
A
B
C
D
E
```

(3)

KU | PS

1

2

5. The grid shows chemical reactions which involve water.

A	$2H_2 + O_2 \longrightarrow 2H_2O$
B	$C_3H_7OH \longrightarrow C_3H_6 + H_2O$
C	$C_{12}H_{22}O_{11} \longrightarrow 12C + 11H_2O$
D	$C_2H_4 + 3O_2 \longrightarrow 2CO_2 + 2H_2O$
E	$CaC_2 + 2H_2O \longrightarrow C_2H_2 + Ca(OH)_2$
F	$CaO + H_2SO_4 \longrightarrow CaSO_4 + H_2O$

(*a*) Identify the neutralization reaction.

A
B
C
D
E
F

(*b*) Dehydration is the removal of water from a compound.

Identify the two dehydration reactions.

A
B
C
D
E
F

(*c*) Identify the reaction which produces an alkene.

A
B
C
D
E
F

KU 1

PS 2

KU 1

(4)

6. The name of six types of reaction are listed in the grid.

A	B	C
addition	condensation	displacement
D	E	F
hydrolysis	polymerisation	redox

(a) Identify the **two** types of reaction which can be applied to the formation of starch from glucose.

A	B	C
D	E	F

(b) Identify the **two** types of reaction represented by the following equation.

$$Zn(s) + Cu^{2+}(Cl^-)_2 \,(aq) \longrightarrow Zn^{2+}(Cl^-)_2 \,(aq) + Cu(s)$$

A	B	C
D	E	F

(4)

KU **2**

PS **2**

PART 2

A total of 40 marks is available in this part of the paper.

7. When magnesium reacts with chlorine, the magnesium loses electrons and the chlorine gains electrons. The ionic compound magnesium chloride is formed.

   (a) Why do atoms gain or lose electrons in chemical reactions?

   _____

   _____

   (b) Magnesium chloride has a high melting point which makes it a solid at room temperature.

   Why do ionic compounds have high melting points?

   _____

   _____

   (c) Two experiments were set up to investigate the conductivity of ionic substances.

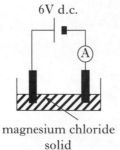
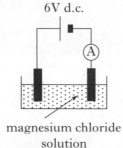

	Does it conduct electricity?	Observation
magnesium chloride solid	NO	No reaction
magnesium chloride solution	YES	Chlorine gas produced at positive electrode

   (i) Explain why sodium choride does not conduct when solid but does when it is dissolved in water to form a solution.

   _____

   _____

   _____

   (ii) Write an ion electron equation for the production of chlorine gas at the positive electrode.

(4)

8. Manganese is added to iron to make an alloy for use in drills.

(a) Why are alloys made?

_____

(b) Manganese can easily be converted into permanganate ions, which are purple coloured.

If placed in a beam of light, the amount of light passing through can be measured.

The percentage of light passing through was measured with different concentrations of permanganate ions.

Concentration of permanganate ions (mol/l)	0·1	0·4	0·8	1·2	1·6	2·0
Light passing through solution (%)	78	54	32	18	10	6

Draw a line graph of these results

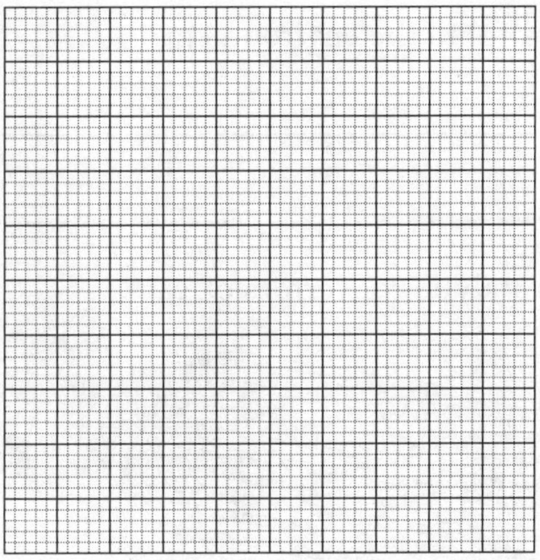

(c) What is the relationship between permanganate concentration and the percentage of light passing through?

_____

_____

(d) When a sample of drill was reacted to form a permanganate solution, the percentage of light which passed through it was 26%.

Use your graph to estimate the concentration of the permanganate solution.

_____

KU | PS

(a) 1

(b) 2

(c) 1

(d) 1

9. Platimum metal is found in the nickel ore millerite.

   (a) The platinum can be extracted simply by heating the ore.

   What does this indicate about the reactivity of platinum?

   _____

   _____

   (b) In millerite the nickel is in the form of nickel sulphide.

   When the ore is heated the following reaction also occurs.

   $$2NiS + 3O_2 \longrightarrow 2NiO + 2SO_2$$

   Calculate the mass of sulphur dioxide produced from 18·1 g of nickel sulphide.

   (c) Why is this reaction harmful to the environment?

   _____

   _____

   (d) Platinum is used in the catalytic convertors of cars.

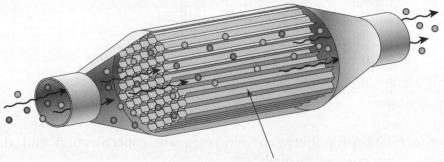

   Catalyst mesh coated with platinum

   (i) What is the purpose of the catalytic convertor?

   _____

   _____

   (ii) Why is the platinum in a mesh rather than in a solid sheet of metal?

   _____

   _____

   (6)

KU	PS
	1
2	
1	
1	
	1

10. (a) The cracking of octane is shown in the following equation.

$$C_8H_{18} \longrightarrow X + C_3H_6$$
$$\text{propene}$$

(i) Give the molecular formula for 'X'.

_____

(ii) Why **must** an alkene be formed in the cracking of an alkane?

_____

_____

(b) Give the general formula for the alkenes.

_____

(c) The alkenes are a homologous series.

Predict the boiling point of the alkene hept-1-ene.

(you may wish to use the data booklet to help you)

_____

(4)

	KU	PS
(a)(i)		1
(a)(ii)	1	
(b)	1	
(c)		1

	KU	PS

11. Many different chloride compounds are used in chemistry.

(a) Tin (IV) chloride can be made in the classroom.

Concentrated hydrochloric acid is dropped onto potassium permanganate to form chlorine gas. The gas is passed through silica gel and then heated as it passes over tin granules. Finally, colourless, tin (IV) chloride liquid is collected in a test tube.

(i) Complete and label the diagram to show how tin (IV) chloride can be formed.

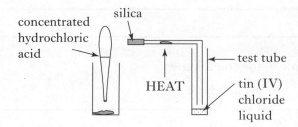

(ii) What type of bonding, indicated by the passage, is found in tin (IV) chloride.

_____

(b) Aluminium chloride, made in a similar way to tin (IV) chloride, is used to make styrene.

The styrene can then be used to form polystyrene as shown below with three styrene monomers.

Why is the term **addition** used in describing this process?

_____

_____

(4)

12. The diagram shows a cell used to produce electricity.

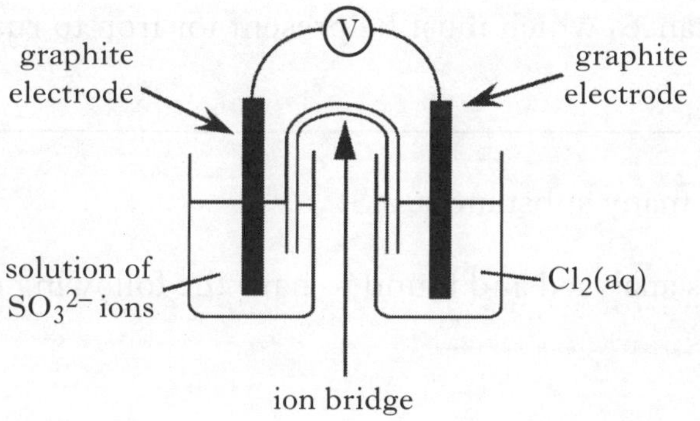

(a) How is electricity produced in a cell?

_____

(b) The reaction in the sulphite beaker is:

$$SO_3^{2-} + H_2O \longrightarrow SO_4^{2-} + 2H^+ + 2e^-$$

On the diagram clearly mark the path and direction of electron flow.

(c) State why this equation represents oxidation.

_____

(d) What would happen to the pH in the left hand beaker containing sulphite?

_____

(e) Write the ion electron equation for the reaction in the chlorine beaker?

(You may wish to use the data booklet to help you.)

(f) Why would silver nitrate not be suitable for use in the ion bridge?

_____

_____

(6)

	KU	PS
(a)	1	
(b)		1
(c)	1	
(d)		1
(e)		1
(f)		1

13. Materials made of iron are susceptible to rusting.

	KU	PS

(a) Name the **two** substances which must be present for iron to rust.

_____

1 (KU)

(b) Rust is a mixture of many substances.

A sample of rust was analysed and found to have the following composition.

Fe   62·3%

O   35·5%

H   2·2%

Calculate the empirical formula of the rust formed.

2 (PS)

(c) When iron corrodes, iron atoms form Fe^{2+} ions.

Fe^{2+} ions can also be oxidised.

Write the formula for the ion formed when Fe^{2+} is oxidised.

_____

1 (KU)

(4)

	KU	PS

14. In order to have healthy growth, plants are supplied with nitrogen in fertilisers.

The fertiliser potassium nitrate can be made with the following process.

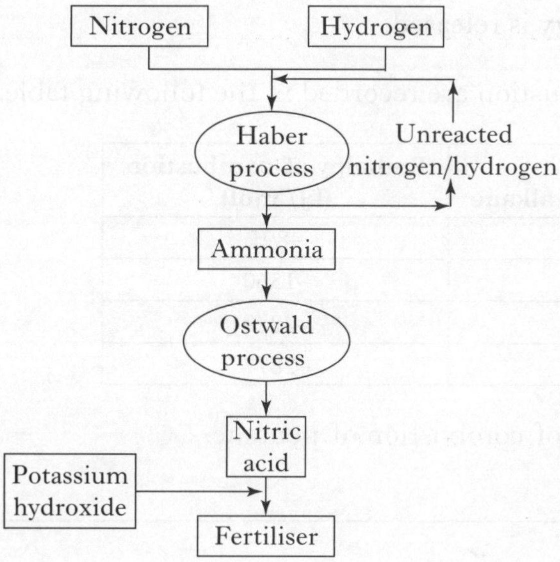

(*a*) What step is taken in the above processes to ensure that no resources are wasted? **PS 1**

(*b*) How could the ammonia gas be separated from the unreacted gases nitrogen and hydrogen?

(You may wish to use the data booklet.) **KU 1**

(*c*) The following reaction takes place in the Ostwald process

$$NH_3 + O_2 \longrightarrow NO + H_2O$$

Balance the above equation. **PS 1**

(*d*) Potassium nitrate fertiliser is made in the reaction;

$$KOH(aq) + HNO_3(aq) \longrightarrow KNO_3(aq) + H_2O(l)$$

(i) Why can KNO_3 be described as a salt? **KU 1**

(ii) How could a solid sample of KNO_3 be obtained? **PS 1**

(5)

15. Alkanes are used as fuels.

The energy released when 1 mole of an alkane is completely burned in pure oxygen is called the Enthalpy of Combustion. By convention, a negative (–) sign is used to show that energy is released.

Some enthalpies of combustion are recorded in the following table.

Name of alkane	Enthalpy of combustion (kJ/ mol)
methane	–891
ethane	–1560
propane	–2220
butane	–2877

(a) Predict the enthalpy of combustion of pentane.

(b) Give a reason why the energy released when burning 1 mole of methane in a gas cooker is less than that given in the above table.

(2)

KU	PS
	1
	1
	1

Worked Answers

1. The first question is normally straightforward and is intended to **help you settle** down. It uses metals to ask you about a number of topics in the course.

1. (*a*) B (iron) and E (platinum) are both needed to obtain this mark

> HINT   A straightforward piece of knowledge which is also found on the data book p8

(*b*) E (platinum)

> HINT   There are a number of catalysts mentioned throughout the course. This question helps you by mentioning the 'Ostwald Process' and explaining that this is used in making nitric acid. Later in the paper only 1 of these facts would be mentioned.
>
> The inclusion of iron in the answer grid is for students who mix up the Haber and Ostwald processes.

TOP EXAM TIP

Learn the common catalysts and where they are used. For example

Catalytic convertors in cars:	platinum, palladium, rhodium
Catalytic cracking:	aluminium oxide
Haber Process (making ammonia):	iron
Ostwald Process (nitric acid manufacture):	platinum

(*c*) A (lithium)

> HINT   If the paper suggests that 'You may want to use the data book to help you' then LOOK UP THE DATA BOOKLET!!
>
> The index tell us that Densities are on page 2. Checking each metal we see that lithium is the least dense. People rushing this question may make two incorrect assumptions:
>
> i)   We know that lead is a dense metal, and so may people will ignore the word 'lowest' and jump to conclusions.
>
> ii) Many people know that aluminium is a 'light' metal and so will put this without checking the data booklet.

2. This question is based on knowledge from unit 1 which is all General. It is made more difficult by asking which is **not** a solute. It is also difficult as it is in an unusual setting and students often get solute and solvent mixed up.

2. D (water)

> HINT   The fruit juice, sugar and carbon dioxide are all getting dissolved and so are solutes. They are dissolved in water, so water is the solvent.

3. This question involves testing your knowledge of the names of the fractions in fractional distillation and their properties.

3. (a) B

(b) E

HINT

In learning the names of the fractions, remember that the top (smallest) is gas and the bottom (largest) is tar (bitumen).

This helps with question b, because it is really asking which is the most difficult to boil (turn from a liquid to a gas), the gas which we get from the taps in the labs or the tar which is used on the roads. As gas is already a gas it must be the bitumen. Also using common sense 'how easy is it to boil the tar on the roads?'

Once we know that gas is at the top and tar is at the bottom we should then just learn the other orders of: petrol, aeroplane fuel, diesel.

4. This question involves looking at the factors which affect the rate of a reaction (temperature, concentration, particle size). It also involves us looking at the equation given for the reaction.

4. (a) B

HINT

The question tells us (and the equation shows us) that the hydrogen peroxide is breaking down. It does not react with any other chemicals.

As there is a catalyst present the rate depends on the hydrogen peroxide coming into contact with the catalyst. As the catalyst is already covered, increasing the volume does not increase the contact so the rate does not increase.

A: Increasing concentration increases the number of H_2O_2 particles in the solution therefore there will be more collisions with the catalyst and so higher rate.

C: Powdering the catalyst increases the surface area and therefore contact and so rate.

D: We know that increasing temperature increases rate.

(b) A and B (**1 mark** each)

From the equation the volume of oxygen produced depends on the amount of hydrogen peroxide you start with. If we increase the volume or concentration we are increasing the actual amount of H_2O_2 and so we will get more oxygen produced.

5. This question is based on our knowledge of acids. For General we need to know that they contain hydrogen ions, but for Credit we have to be more precise (see answer E).

5. B and E (**1 mark** each)

HINT

We should know that acids conduct electricity and react with magnesium. This rules out answers A and C. Answer D is wrong because only hydrochloric acid will give chlorine.

TOP EXAM TIP

It helps if you know the formula of the 3 acids commonly used in questions:

hydrochloric acid (H^+Cl^-), nitric Acid ($H^+NO_3^-$) and sulphuric acid ($(H^+)_2SO_4^{2-}$)

 6. This question may put you off as you have not met it in class, but if you look at the marks, it is all problem solving.

6. (*a*) C + E (both needed for **1 mark**)

> **HINT**
>
> A and B are obviously incorrect as they have different numbers of C atoms.
>
> It is useful to work out the molecular formulae of the others.
>
> C C_3H_6O D C_3H_8O E C_3H_6O

(*b*) D

> **HINT**
>
> We can see from the hint to part (a) that D fits this general formula.
>
> It is still helpful to check that A and B are incorrect
>
> A CH_2O_2 B $C_2H_4O_2$

 7. This question requires you to know what will happen in chemical reactions over several units

7.   C and F (**1 mark** each)

> **HINT**
>
> To tackle this question I suggest that you go through each box and identify ones in which you are confident the chemicals do or do **not** react together.
>
> A   This is from topic 11: using carbon to reduce metal oxides into metals.
>
> B   This is from topic 11: reactions of metals with water, and topic 3 where we know that Group 1 are very reactive metals.
>
> C   This is from topic 10: copper is below sodium in the electrochemical series and so can**not** displace it from its compounds.
>
> D   This is from topic 5: combustion is the reaction of hydrocarbons with oxygen
>
> E   This is from topics 9, 10 and 11: magnesium is higher than hydrogen in the electrochemical series so it can displace it. Therefore magnesium will react with acids.
>
> F   This is from topics 9, 10 and 11: silver is lower than hydrogen in the electrochemical series so it can**not** displace it. Therefore silver will not react with acids.

 8. This question is similar to question 7. Although it is problem solving it does rely on applying knowledge using the electrochemical series page 7 of the data booklet and relating it to the reactivity series.

8.   A and D (**1 mark** each)

HINT

1 and 3 are above copper in the electrochemical series as electrons go from them to copper.

2 and 4 are below copper in the electrochemical series as electrons go from copper to the metal.

1 and 3 > copper > 2 and 4

The bigger the voltage, the larger the difference in position in the electrochemical series therefore:

metal 3 (1·0V) is higher above copper than metal 1 (0·5V)

metal 2 (0·3V) is lower below copper than metal 4 (0·2V)

We can also relate position in electrochemical series to reactivity.

Therefore reactivity:

most reactive is 3 > 1 > copper > 4 > 2 least reactive

Therefore E is incorrect because the voltage depends on how far apart metals are in the electrochemical series.

B is incorrect as the more reactive metals are found as compounds.

C is incorrect as the least reactive are the easiest to get from their compounds.

TOP EXAM TIP

The electrochemical series on page 7 of the data booklet has many uses.

A substance will only displace ions of a substance below it in the electrochemical series.

Electrons will always flow from the higher substance towards the lower substance.

The bigger the difference in the electrochemical series, the bigger the voltage produced.

9. A problem solving question using knowledge of the Periodic Table, transition metals and the reactions of acids.

9. A and E (**1 mark** each)

HINT

A Transition metals have pH's 1 and 3 therefore correct

B Sulphates have pH 3 and 7 therefore incorrect

C Sodium salts have pH 7 and 10 therefore incorrect

D Group 1 metal salts have pHs 7, 10, 11 therefore incorrect

E Carbonic acid gives carbonates pH 10 and 11 therefore correct

10. This question relating melting point and boiling point is often found difficult.

10. C

HINT

Below its melting point, a substance will be a solid

Above its boiling point, a substance will be a gas

A substance is a liquid if the temperature is between the MP and BP.

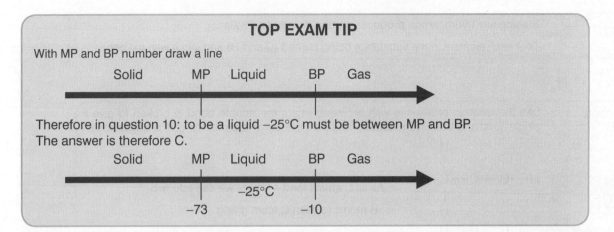

TOP EXAM TIP

With MP and BP number draw a line

Solid   MP   Liquid   BP   Gas

Therefore in question 10: to be a liquid $-25°C$ must be between MP and BP.
The answer is therefore C.

Solid   MP   Liquid   BP   Gas

          $-25°C$

-73 -10

11. This question asks you to relate atomic structure to the relative atomic mass.

11. (*a*) Isotopes

(*b*) There is more ^{39}K than ^{41}K

> **HINT**   The relative atomic mass is always closest to the most common (abundant) isotope.

(*c*) Protons   19

Neutrons   20

Electrons   18

> **HINT**
> The bottom number is the Atomic Number: the number of protons; 19
>
> The top number is the Mass Number: the Number of protons + neutrons
>
> Therefore number of neutrons = Mass Number − Atomic number = 39 − 19 = 20
>
> As the ion has a charge of + there must be 1 more positive proton than negative electron. Therefore there are 18 electrons.

12. A problem-solving question. It uses knowledge of hydrocarbons and alkenes in particular to solve problems about a new homologous series.

12. (*a*) C_nH_{2n-2}

> **HINT**
> General formulae are always based on C_nH_{2n}. To get the correct number of hydrogen atoms, add or subtract from 2n.
>
> | Formula | 2n | number of hydrogens | therefore H is |
> |---------|-----|---------------------|----------------|
> | C_2H_2 | $2 \times 2 = 4$ | 2 | $2n - 2$ |
> | C_3H_4 | $2 \times 3 = 6$ | 4 | $2n - 2$ |
> | C_4H_6 | $2 \times 4 = 8$ | 6 | $2n - 2$ |

(*b*) Carbon dioxide (CO_2) and water (H_2O).

> **HINT**
> Burning any hydrocarbon produces carbon dioxide and water.
> Take each element in the substance being burned (C and H) and join it with oxygen.

(c) C_3H_8

> **HINT**
> Like the reaction of alkenes with bromine, where the double bond is broken to give a single bond and bromine is added, here the triple bond is broken to give a single bond.
>
> ```
>             H
>             |
>  H — C — C — C — H
>             |
>             H
> ```
> As all C atoms form 4 bonds we can add two
> H atoms to each C atom giving
>
> ```
>      H   H   H
>      |   |   |
>  H — C — C — C — H
>      |   |   |
>      H   H   H
> ```
> molecular formula C_3H_8

(d) We are told that it has a double bond.

We must turn it into a ring or we will need too many hydrogen atoms.

```
 H — C ═ C — H
      \   /
   H — C — H
```

> ★ **13.** During the exam there is always a question involving drawing or completing a graph. This question also involves completing the apparatus.

13. (a)

delivery tube · carbon dioxide · measuring cylinder · calcium carbonate · hydrochloride acid · water

1 mark correct diagram **1 mark** correct labels

> **HINT**
> The gas has to be
> - <u>collected</u> so it can be bubbled through water (as it does not dissolve easily)
> - <u>measured</u>. Make sure the measuring cylinder is labelled and there are marks on it to show it has a scale. A test tube will not get the marks as it does not measure volume. The measuring cylinder must be vertical or it would not be possible to read the scale properly.

TOP EXAM TIP

If you are making a gas and you want to measure the volume, you may find it easier to connect the delivery tube to a labelled gas syringe.

Gas syringe

(b)

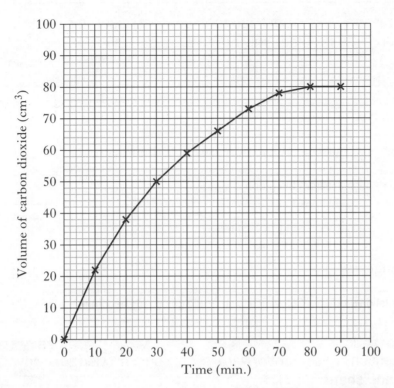

Labels with units X axis: Time (min.); Y axis: volume of carbon dioxide(cm³) $(\frac{1}{2})$

Scale: each box on an axis must be worth the same and the graph must take up at least half the graph paper scale $(\frac{1}{2})$

Plotting the points $(\frac{1}{2})$

Joining the points or a line of best fit $(\frac{1}{2})$

(c)

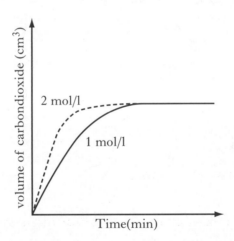

The graph must be steeper but must level off at the same volume $(2 \times \frac{1}{2})$

> **HINT**
>
> We have increased the concentration so the reaction will be faster. Therefore the line is steeper.
>
> The acid was in excess in experiment 1, meaning that all the calcium carbonate is used up. The mass of calcium carbonate has not changed, so the final volume will not change.

> **TOP EXAM TIP**
>
> If a reaction is faster the graph will be steeper. You could be asked 'how can you tell that the reaction is faster?' You should answer 'the graph is steeper'.

14. This question asks about fermentation and uses it to ask some straightforward problem-solving questions.

14. (*a*) Biological catalyst

(*b*) As pH increases zymase activity increases and then decreases

> *HINT* — We can deduce this from the graph

(*c*) Hydrolysis

(*d*) Green to orange-red

> *HINT* — Fermentation produces CO_2 which is an acidic gas so pH becomes acidic.

15. This question is a straightforward test of your knowledge of covalent bonds and shape.

15. (*a*)

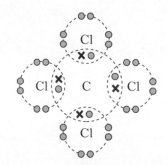

(*b*)

Cl
|
C......Cl
Cl   or
Cl
Cl
        Cl
        |
        C
    Cl   Cl
        Cl

> *HINT* — You must try and show the **shape**, so the following is incorrect as it does not show the actual tetrahedral shape
>
> Cl
> |
> Cl—C—Cl
> |
> Cl

TOP EXAM TIP

There are three basic shapes you may be asked to show and they depend on the number of atoms attached to a central atom.

4 atoms around a central atom gives a tetrahedral

3 atoms around a central atom gives the following

2 atoms around a central atom gives the following

16. A question on corrosion made difficult as it looks at where the electrons go.

16. (*a*) Hydroxide

> **HINT** If you have forgotten this it is on p7 of the data booklet, where we see that hydroxide ions (OH⁻) are formed.

(*b*) Rusting will increase

(*c*) Tin is below iron in the electrochemical series

> **HINT** Iron will sacrificially protect tin, therefore giving electrons to tin and so corroding itself.

17. A straightforward question on making polymers and the problems of burning them.

17. (*a*)

> **HINT** To join 3 monomers copy them out without the double bonds then join them together.

(*b*) HCl

HINT > The Cl is the clue that the toxic fumes are HCl.

18. This question on the formation of ammonia starts requires you to think about what is actually happening in the process.

18. (*a*) The reaction is reversible.

HINT > The equation for the reaction is written with arrows pointing towards the products and reactants. This is because, once ammonia is formed, some of it breaks down to re-form the reactants, so 100% ammonia is never achieved.

(*b*) At higher temperatures less ammonia is produced.

HINT > Although the reaction would be faster at higher temperatures, because the reaction is reversible, much less nitrogen and hydrogen is turned into ammonia and so overall less ammonia is formed.

(*c*) This can be used to heat up the reaction.

HINT > Exothermic means energy is released. This energy can be used to heat up its own reaction.

19. This question requires some analysis of data to solve problems, combined with some knowledge of ions and cells.

19. (*a*) Colourless

HINT > Although sodium dichromate is orange, sodium chloride is colourless.
>
> Therefore the sodium ion is colourless.

(*b*) $(Na^+)_2Cr_2O_7^{2-}$

HINT > In ionic formulae you must show the charges on the ions.
>
> Sodium is in group 1 so it forms an ion with a charge of 1+
>
> Dichromate is one of the ions given in the table at the foot of page 4 in the data booklet.

TOP EXAM TIP

In an ionic formula the charges on the ions must cancel out.

For example Na^+ and $Cr_2O_7^{2-}$

There is one positive charge and two negative charges.

There must be two of the (+) positive ions to cancel the (2–) charge on the negative ion. So $(Na^+)_2Cr_2O_7^{2-}$

TOP EXAM TIP

If in a formula there is more than 1 of an ion, put it in brackets.

So two Na^+ ions is written as $(Na^+)_2$ and not Na^+_2

(c) (i) Pink

HINT

Cobalt is a metal so it must form positive ions.

Positive ions will be attracted to the negative electrode.

Pink colour appears at the positive electrode so cobalt ions are pink.

(ii) To complete the circuit

HINT   The sodium nitrate is serving the same purpose as an ion bridge in a cell.

(iii) Barium ions would form an insoluble solid with sulphate ions.

TOP EXAM TIP

In any electrical circuit, if you are ever asked to choose a chemical for an ion bridge or to complete a circuit, ensure that it does not react with any of the other chemicals to form an insoluble solid.

Look up page 5 in the data booklet.

20. This question involves analysis one of the practicals carried out during the course. It then uses knowledge of concentration and balanced equations to carry out two calculations.

20. (a) The indicator will change colour.

(b) The first titration is to find a rough volume.

HINT   The volumes used to calculate the average must be within $0.2 \ cm^3$ of each other.

(c) $n = c \times v$

$$= 0.1 \times \frac{21.4}{1000}$$

$$= 0.1 \times 0.0214$$

$$= 0.00214 \ mol$$

TOP EXAM TIP

The triangle $\frac{n}{c \times v}$ is used when talking about solutions.

n = number of moles

c = concentration

v = volume

Remember: Volume is always in **litres** so divide any volume in cm^3 by 1000

Concentration is in **mol/l**.

The question may expect you to know that a number is the concentration from the units mol/l

(d) 0·00428 mol

From the equation 1 mole of sulphuric acid reacts with 2 moles of sodium hydroxide.

From part c we have 0·00214 moles of H_2SO_4

therefore $2 \times 0·00214 = 0·00428$ mol of NaOH

or it could be written

$$H_2SO_4 + 2NaOH \longrightarrow Na_2SO_4 + 2H_2O$$

1 mole   2 moles

0·00214   0·00428

21. This question looks at the extraction of iron and aluminium from their ores

21. (a) Reduction

(b) To ensure the iron is molten (a liquid)

> **HINT**
>
> The temperature was mentioned and you were directed to the data booklet.
>
> Temperatures in the data booklet refer to melting and boiling points.
>
> Looking up iron we see its MP is 1535°C., so the temperature must be above this to keep it molten.

(c) (i) Aluminum is a reactive metal (so forms unreactive compounds)

> **HINT**
>
> The more reactive metals form the most stable compounds.
>
> So compounds of aluminium and above can only be broken down to give the metal using electrolysis.

(ii) Chlorine

> **HINT**
>
> Metals form positive ions and non-metals form negative ions.
>
> As opposites attract, it must be the negative ion (non-metal) attracted to the positive electrode.
>
> So the chloride ion is attracted and chlorine is given off.

TOP EXAM TIP

Be careful when talking about ions:

The names of metals are the same for the elements and the ions,

i.e. aluminium metal and aluminium ions.

The names of non-metals are changed to end in –ide when we talk about the ions. i.e. chlorine gas but chloride ions.

1. The first question in this paper is on problem solving. It starts off with a simple question on the Periodic Table and gradually gets more difficult as it moves on to electron arrangement of ions and then formulae.

1. (*a*) A+D (both needed for **1 mark**)

> HINT   Elements in the same Group (vertical column) have similar chemical properties.

TOP EXAM TIP

The data booklet (pages 1, 2, 3 and 8) give the numbers of each group.

(*b*) B

> HINT
>
> Non-metals **gain** electrons to form ions with a stable electron arrangement.
>
> Metals **lose** electrons to form ions with a stable electron arrangement.
>
> Ne has electron arrangement 2,8
>
> The elements listed become:
>
> | | | | | | |
> |---|---|---|---|---|---|
> | Li^+ | 2 | O^{2-} | 2,8 | P^{3-} | 2,8,8 |
> | K^+ | 2,8,8 | Cl^- | 2,8,8 | Ca^{2+} | 2,8,8 |

TOP EXAM TIP

Elements form ions to obtain the electron arrangement of the **nearest** Noble Gas.

i.e. Ne is atomic number 10: Therefore non metals 6-9 and metals 11-13 will form ions with the same electron arrangement.

(*c*) Identify the two elements which form an ionic compound with the formula of the type XY_2, where **X** is the metal.

E+F (both needed for **1 mark**)

> HINT
>
> If the formula is XY_2, with X being a metal and XY_2 being an ionic compound, X must be X^{2+} and Y must be Y^-.
>
> Looking at hint to part (b):   X must be $F(Ca^{2+})$ Y must be E (Cl^-)

TOP EXAM TIP

Metals lose electrons to become positive ions

Non-metals gain electrons to become negative ions.

The number of electrons lost or gained (valency) depends on which group they are in.

Group	1	2	3	4	5	6	7
Charge	+	2+	3+	4+/–	3–	2–	–
Valency	1	2	3	4	3	2	1

To get a formula we swap the size of the charge (valency) so that the charges cancel out.

i.e. X^{2+} Y^- will have formula $(X^{2+})(Y^-)_2$

valency 2 ⤫ 1

Thus we do this backwards for question 1c

	Formula	XY_2	
Therefore	X		Y_2
Valency	2 ⤫		1
Group	2 or 6		1 or 7
Group	2		7

X is a metal so Group 2; Y is a non-metal therefore

X is F (Ca) Y is E (Cl)

---

2. This question requires a knowledge of fair experiments and the reactivity series.

2. (a) A + F (both needed for **1 mark**)

> **HINT** To show the effect of temperature the **only** difference between the two experiments must be temperature

(b) C

> **HINT** From the reactivity series copper and metals below it will not react with acids.

---

3. This question involves looking at molecular formulae, knowledge of General Formulae and the ability to relate relative formula mass to the structural formula.

3. (a) B

> **HINT**
>
> Isomers: same molecular formula, different structural formula
>
> You could work out the molecular formula for each hydrocarbon.
>
> A C_4H_{10} B C_3H_6 C C_4H_{10}
>
> D C_3H_6 E C_3H_8 F C_2H_6
>
> Or a quicker way is:
>
> It must be B or E as they are the only other hydrocarbons with 3 carbon atoms.
>
> B has 6 hydrogen atoms and E has 8 hydrogen atoms.
>
> Therefore answer is B.

(b) E

> **HINT**
>
> C has relative atomic mass 12, H has relative atomic mass 1 (see data booklet p4)
>
> There must be less than 4 C atoms, as $4 \times 12 = 48$: giving mass above 44
>
> 2 C atoms would have mass 24, therefore needing 20 H atoms: not possible
>
> 3 C atoms ($3 \times 13 = 36$) will need 8 H atoms ($8 \times 1 = 8$): mass 44: Answer E

(c) A+E (both needed for **1 mark**)

> **HINT**
>
> C_5H_{12} fits General Formula C_nH_{2n+2}: alkanes
>
> A and E fit this formula
>
> (It cannot be B,C or F as they are alkenes)
>
> (It cannot be D as it is a cycloalkane)

4. This problem-solving question looks at the electrochemical series (unit 10) and electron flow in a cell. It also requires knowledge of ferroxyl indicator (unit 12).

4. (a) B

> **HINT**
>
> Electrons always flow from a metal higher in the electrochemical series to one below it. Referring to data booklet (p7) this gives answers A, B or E
>
> Ferroxyl goes blue when Fe^{2+} ions are present.
>
> Therefore Fe is losing electrons to form Fe^{2+}, so metal A must be Fe.

(b) D

> **HINT**
>
> The largest voltage will be produced by metals furthest apart in the electrochemical series.
>
> Referring to data booklet p7 we see this is answer D (magnesium and copper)

5. This question requires knowledge of the reactions of acids and the ability to use the data booklet and identify combination of ions which will produce insoluble salts.

5. (a) D

> **HINT**
>
> A base is a substance which neutralises an acid.
>
> (The most common are oxides, hydroxides and carbonates.)

TOP EXAM TIP

There are 4 reactions of acids where they are neutralised.

Acid	+	metal	$\longrightarrow$	salt	+	H_2		
Acid	+	metal oxide	$\longrightarrow$	salt	+	H_2O		
Acid	+	metal hydroxide (alkali)	$\longrightarrow$	salt	+	H_2O		
Acid	+	metal carbonate	$\longrightarrow$	salt	+	H_2O	+	CO_2

(b) C + D

> **HINT**
>
> The data book p 5 gives solubilities.
> Take the first part of each compound and combine it with the second part from the other boxes:
> Sodium:　　　vs with all the other compounds
> i.e. sodium bromide, sodium chloride, sodium iodide, sodium carbonate, sodium nitrate
> Ammonium:　　vs with the other compounds
> Barium:　　　vs with all others except carbonate (in D)
> Lithium:　　　vs with the other compounds
> Potassium:　　vs with all the other compounds
> Therefore C and D will form insoluble barium carbonate.

6. A problem solving question which requires the analysis of data in a table to look for trends.

6.　C, D

> **HINT**
>
> Take each statement and check it:
>
> The table indicates statement
> A:　BP increases as density increases **except** 13 to 17 –210 to –220:　　incorrect
> B:　Ar density 18 is greater than N_2; 13 and F_2; 17;　　incorrect
> C:　As relative formula mass increases density increases;　　correct
> D:　As relative formula mass increases BP increases **except**
> 　　nitrogen mass 28 BP –210 to fluorine mass 38 BP –220　　correct

TOP EXAM TIP

Remember if the temperature is negative (below zero) then as the number gets smaller the temperature is rising i.e. –25°C is higher than –50°C

–100 –75 –50 –25　0　25　50　75　100

7. This should be a straight forward question on the pollution problems of fuels but part (a) is also applicable to unit 14 fertilisers.

7.　(a) D

> **HINT**
>
> In lightning storms the nitrogen in the air forms nitrogen oxides.
> This also happens in petrol engines, where a sparkplug is used to ignite the petrol in air.

(b) A

> **HINT**
>
> CO is produced by the incomplete combustion of fuel in a poor supply of air.
>
> Increasing the air to fuel ratio, means increasing the air (as it is mentioned first).
>
> With enough air we get complete combustion, therefore CO_2 instead of CO.

TOP EXAM TIP

When talking about ratios the description applies to the first chemical named.

Increasing air : fuel   means increasing the amount of air compared to fuel

Increasing fuel : air   means increasing the amount of fuel compared to air.

8. This question on corrosion seems straightforward but some of the statements need to be read very carefully.

8.   A, D

> **HINT**
>
> Rusting is an oxidation reaction and salt water does increase the speed, as it is an electrolyte and so it is a good conductor.
>
> B is incorrect as a coating prevents water and air reaching the iron and so slows down rusting.
>
> C is incorrect as copper is lower than iron in the electrochemical series and so the iron would actually sacrificially protect the copper.
>
> E is incorrect. Although ferroxyl indicator does turn pink during rusting, this is where the water and oxygen are reacting and not the iron. The iron turns the indicator blue when Fe^{2+} is formed.

9. A question which requires you to apply your knowledge of isomers (topic 6) to carbohydrates (Topic 15)

9.   (*a*)   C and E (both needed for **1 mark**)

> **HINT**
>
> The two disaccharides are maltose and sucrose. As disaccharides have the same molecular formula they are both isomers of lactose.

    (*b*)   E

> **HINT**
>
> Sucrose does not react with Benedicts' solution or starch.

TOP EXAM TIP

In carbohydrates the test results are:

Glucose, fructose maltose and lactose turn Benedicts' from blue to brick red.

Starch turns iodine blue/black.

Only sucrose gives no reaction with **both** Benedicts' and iodine.

10. A question on isotopes which requires you to know what is represented in nuclide notation and what information Mass Number and Atomic Number give. It then leads on to another question on the shapes of molecules.

10. (*a*) (i)   isotopes

  (ii)   14

> **HINT**   The average atomic mass is closer to 14, so it must be the most common isotope.

(*a*) (iii)

Type of atom	Number of protons	Number of neutrons
$^{14}_{7}N$	7	7
$^{15}_{7}N$	7	8

> **HINT**   The bottom number is the Atomic Number (number of protons)
>
> The top number is the Mass Number (number of protons + neutrons)
>
> Therefore number of protons = Mass Number – Atomic Number

(*b*)

> **HINT**   The diagram must make an attempt to show the actual shape, therefore
>
> $$H—N—H$$
> $$|$$
> $$H$$
>
> is not a correct answer.

11. A question on the production of alcohol made more difficult by bringing in reactions of alkenes in an unfamiliar situation.

11. (*a*) (i)   Fermentation/anaerobic respiration

  (ii)   Decreases/slows down/stops

> **HINT**   We would normally expect rate to increase with temperature but as enzymes have an optimum temperature, the rate would slow down above 37°C and would eventually stop when the enzyme's shape is changed.

(*b*) (i)   Addition/hydration

> **HINT**   This is similar to the addition of bromine when it is decolourised by alkenes.
>
> If you ask yourself what has been done to the alkene you can see that atoms have been **added** to it. It is therefore addition.
>
> As water is being added it can also be called hydration.

(ii) distillation

> **HINT**
>
> Normally this question would be used to explain how to increase the concentration of alcohol by distilling it to get 100% alcohol and then diluting it.
>
> But it is the same principle: distillation is used to separate any mixture of liquids with different boiling points.

12. A question on polymers made more difficult using an unfamiliar structure which needs a key.

12. (*a*)

> **HINT**
>
> The monomers are always based on ethene.
>
> Find the repeating unit and put in a dotted line.
>
> Then draw the repeating unit with a double bond but without the connecting bonds.
>
>
> repeating unit

(*b*) Thermoplastic or thermopolymer

> **HINT**
>
> The other type is thermosetting. If it contains the word set, it will not change shape on heating (i.e. it will not melt).

(*c*) Carbon monoxide

> **HINT**
>
> You need to look at the side group. This is the main difference between the addition polymers (polymers based on ethene).
>
> It contains a large number of carbon atoms so when burning there are unlikely to be enough oxygen molecules to make carbon dioxide.
>
> The answer cannot be HCl or cyanide as the polymer does not contain Cl or CN respectively.

TOP EXAM TIP

Do not get confused over melting and burning.

Melting means changing state (shape) when heated.

Burning means reacting with oxygen and giving out energy.

Any polymer can burn but only thermoplastics can melt.

 13. A question asking you to draw a graph. Use your graph to work back and estimate a result and then draw a conclusion on a trend from the graph.

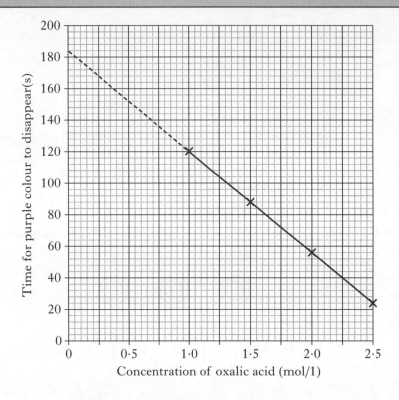

13. (*a*) (i) Draw a line graph of the results.

Labels with units X axis; concentration of oxalic acid (mol/l)

Y axis; time for purple colour to disappear(s) $\left(\frac{1}{2}\right)$

Scale: each box on an axis must be worth the same and the graph must take up at least half the graph paper scale $\left(\frac{1}{2}\right)$

Plotting the points $\left(\frac{1}{2}\right)$

Joining the points or a line of best fit $\left(\frac{1}{2}\right)$

TOP EXAM TIP

When drawing a useful reminder tool is: LUST

L	Label	(get these from the table headings)
U	Units	(get these from the table headings)
S	Scale	(the graph should take up at least half of the graph paper)
T	The graph	(plot the points and join them or do a line of best fit)

(ii) 152+/−2s

Draw a line back to see the reading at 0·5 mol/l

HINT — Look at dashed line back to 0·5 mol/l

(b) As concentration increases speed increases (or it takes less time)

14. A straightforward question on balancing equations and the pH of ammonia.

14. (a) $2NaOH + (NH_4)_2SO_4 \longrightarrow Na_2SO_4 + 2NH_3 + 2H_2O$

(b) Ammonia would turn moist pH paper blue/alkaline/pH above 7

15. This is a problem-solving question asking you to predict a structure from examples given and then use data to identify trends and make predictions.

15. (a)

H—C—C—C—C—N with H atoms and NH_2 group

HINT — To get the above structure just add 1 C onto the third amine, and ensure that the number of bonds is correct.

(b) (i) As the number of C atoms increases the BP increases

(ii) 125 − 135°C

HINT — The first increase in BP is 32°C then 28°C and lastly 26°C.

A reasonable guess would be the next increase is 26°C giving 127°C.

But any increase between 22°C and 32°C would get the mark.

16. This calculation question involves using the triangles for solutions and for mass.

16. (a) n = c × v

= 4 × 50/1000

= 4 × 0·050

= 0·20 mol

HINT

The triangle used is

$\frac{n}{c \times v}$

(b) (i) 0·10 mol

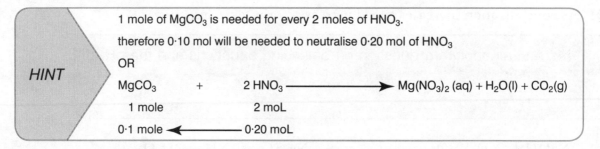

HINT

1 mole of $MgCO_3$ is needed for every 2 moles of HNO_3.

therefore 0·10 mol will be needed to neutralise 0·20 mol of HNO_3

OR

$MgCO_3$ +   2 HNO_3 ⟶ $Mg(NO_3)_2$ (aq) + H_2O(l) + CO_2(g)

1 mole   2 moL

0·1 mole ⟵ 0·20 moL

(ii) 8·45g

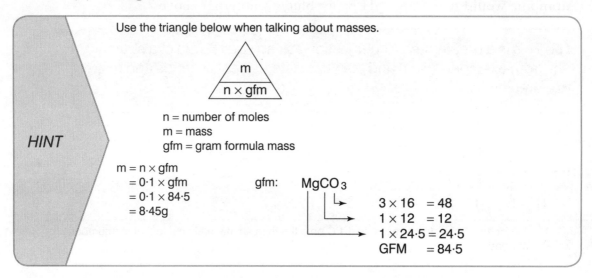

HINT

Use the triangle below when talking about masses.

$\frac{m}{n \times gfm}$

n = number of moles
m = mass
gfm = gram formula mass

m = n × gfm
  = 0·1 × gfm
  = 0·1 × 84·5
  = 8·45g

gfm: $MgCO_3$

3 × 16 = 48
1 × 12 = 12
1 × 24·5 = 24·5
GFM   = 84·5

(c) Bubbles/ gas/effervescence would have been observed.

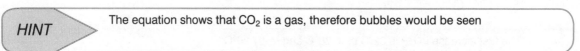

HINT

The equation shows that CO_2 is a gas, therefore bubbles would be seen

(d) To ensure that all of the acid had reacted

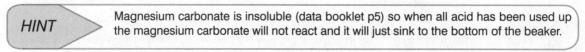

HINT

Magnesium carbonate is insoluble (data booklet p5) so when all acid has been used up the magnesium carbonate will not react and it will just sink to the bottom of the beaker.

17. A question on the production of ammonia and a problem solving element on the advantages of natural nitrogen fixation

17. (*a*) Haber

(*b*) It will save on energy needed to produce fertilisers.

> **HINT**
>
> Two industrial processes are discussed in standard grade when making fertilisers: the Haber and the Ostwald Processes.
>
> The Ostwald process is exothermic and the heat produced can be used to keep it going. The Haber Process needs to be heated and so energy is needed.

TOP EXAM TIP

When asked for an advantage of any process do **not** answer 'to save money'.
Always answer in terms of saving energy.

18. A question which involves naming compounds and salts.
The calculation can be done in three ways.

18. (*a*) Lead suphide

> **HINT**
>
> Remember that when naming two-element compounds, the name of the first element stays the same as in the Periodic Table and the name of the second element has its ending changed to –ide.

(*b*) Aluminium chloride

> **HINT**
>
> The hydrogen from an acid is replaced with the metal ion (or ammonium) when a salt is formed.

TOP EXAM TIP

The salts formed from the common acids are

Hydrochloric acid	HCl	chlorides
Nitric acid	HNO_3	nitrates
Sulphuric acid	H_2SO_4	sulphates

(*c*) 11·2 tons

The calculation can be tackled in three ways

Method 1 In the same way as question 16 parts (a) and (b)

And do the question in 4 parts each worth a ½ **mark**

1) Try to work out what you are asked: the number of moles of haematite (Fe_2O_3).

2) Work out the number of moles of the substance you are told about, Fe_2O_3.

3) Use the balanced equation to work out how many moles of iron this will make.

4) Knowing the number of moles of iron calculate the mass using the mass triangle.

    1)   work out mass of Fe

    Using triangle below when talking about masses.

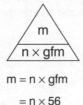

$$m = n \times gfm$$

$$= n \times 56$$

We do not know 'n' so work out 'n' for the other substance we are told about.

    2)   Work out the number of moles of haematite (Fe_2O_3).

    number of moles of Fe_2O_3: $n = m/gfm$

    mass = 16 tons: use 16g for questions and turn back into tons at the end gfm: Fe_2O_3

$$3 \times 16 = \ \ 48$$
$$2 \times 56 = 112$$
$$GFM = 160$$

$m = n/gfm = 16/160 = 0.1$ mole

    3)   Use the balanced equation to work out how many moles of iron this will make

$$Fe_2O_3 \ + \ 3CO \longrightarrow 2Fe \ + \ 3CO_2$$

balanced   1 mole   makes   2 moles

equation tells   0.1 mole   will make   0.2 moles

    4)   Knowing the number of moles of iron, calculate the mass using the mass triangle.

$m = n \times GFM = 0.2 \times 56 = 11.2g$

As the question was in tons, give the answer in tons therefore **11.2 tons**

Method 2 As method 1, but set out differently:

$$Fe_2O_3 + 3CO \longrightarrow 2Fe + 3CO_2$$

$m = n \times gfm$ gfm Fe : 56 (data book p4)

$= n \times 56$

$n = m/gfm$

$= 16/160$ Fe_2O_3

$= 0.1$ mole $\longrightarrow$ 0.2 mole $3 \times 16 = \ \ 48$

s $m = n \times gfm$ $2 \times 56 = 112$

                           $= 0.2 \times 56$ $GFM = 160$

                           $= 11.2$

The masses were in tons, therefore answer **11.2 tons**

Method 3 Using gfm, the balanced equation and direct proportion:

$$Fe_2O_3 \ + \ 3CO \longrightarrow 2Fe \quad + 3CO_2$$

Using GFM	160g	2(56g)
So	160g	112g
Therefore	16g	11.2g
Therefore	16 tons	11.2 tons

(*d*) Mercury, silver, gold

| HINT | The less reactive metals form the least stable compounds and as such the compounds are easily broken down to give the metal, by heat alone. |

19. A question on cells where the data booklet is very useful.

19. (*a*)

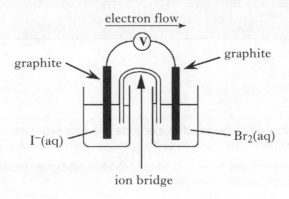

HINT	We have an ion electron equation so look up p7 of data booklet.
	Electrons always flow from substance higher in electrochemical series to the lower substance. So electrons flow from iodide to bromine.
	Also we are told that iodide ions are oxidised (losing electrons) so electrons will flow to the bromine through the easiest path (the wires and the voltmeter).

(*b*) (i) To complete the circuit.

TOP EXAM TIP
The purpose of the electrolyte /salt bridge/ion bridge is always to complete the circuit.

(ii) The silver ions would form a precipitate and so the current could not flow.

| HINT | Data book p5 shows that the only soluble silver compound is silver nitrate. |

TOP EXAM TIP
Silver solutions should therefore not be used as the electrolyte because they will form a precipitate with most negatively charged ions. (In this question they would form the solids silver iodide and silver bromide.)

(*c*) $Br_2 + 2e^- \longrightarrow 2\,Br^-$

| HINT | Use data booklet p7. |

TOP EXAM TIP

If you have to write an ion electron equation for a reduction, look up the data booklet p7 and see if it is written there. If it is just copy it.

If you need an ion electron equation for an oxidation just reverse the reduction reaction.

i.e. if reduction is $\quad\quad\quad Br_2 + 2e^- \longrightarrow 2\,Br^-$

then oxidation will be $\quad 2Br^- \longrightarrow 2\,Br_2 + 2e^-$

20. This question takes your knowledge of conductivity and asks you to use it in the analysis of a conductivity experiment.

20. (*a*) electrolysis

(*b*) (i) nitric acid

> **HINT**
> As bubbles formed at the negative electrode, the ions being attracted must have been positively charged. They are likely to be hydrogen from the acid.
>
> Sucrose would not give a gas and silver chloride would give chlorine gas but this would have been at the positive electrode.

(ii) bubbles of gas (chlorine/Cl_2)

> **HINT**
> The solid is likely to be nickel metal.
>
> Therefore negatively charged chloride ions will be attracted to the positive electrode and form chlorine gas.

(iii) covalent

> **HINT**
> It must be covalent as covalent solutions do not conduct electricity and in Experiment C the bulb did not light, indicating that it did not conduct electricity.

1. This question is similar to Q1 from practice paper 2 with an emphasis on knowing the names of Groups in the Periodic Table and calculating formulae without charges.

1. (*a*) C + F (both needed for **1 mark**)

> *HINT*
>
> Elements form ions to obtain the electron arrangement of the **nearest** Noble Gas.
>
> i.e. Argon is atomic number 18 therefore: non-metals 14–17 and metals 19–20 will form ions with the same electron arrangement.

(*b*) B and C (both needed for **1 mark**)

> *HINT*
>
> Halogens are Group 7. Check the data book pages.

TOP EXAM TIP

You need to know the names of 3 Groups:

Group 1	Alkali metals
Group 7	Halogens
Group 0(8)	Noble Gases

(*c*) A and E (both needed for **1 mark**)

> *HINT*
>
> This is like Q1c from practice paper B but we are ignoring charges as it does not say 'ionic formula'.
>
> To obtain the formula we cross over the valency.
> Valency depends on the Group in the Periodic Table.
>
> | Group | 1 | 2 | 3 | 4 | 5 | 6 | 7 |
> |---|---|---|---|---|---|---|---|
> | Valency | 1 | 2 | 3 | 4 | 3 | 2 | 1 |
>
> i.e. phosphorus chloride
>
> valency $\overset{P}{3}\diagdown\diagup\overset{H}{1}$
> formula PH_3
>
> We work backwards   if formula $X\diagdown\diagup Y_3$
>
> Then valency $3\diagdown\diagup 1$
> Therefore Group   3/5   1/7
>
> In this question
>
> Formula is X_2Y_3 therefore this comes from $X\diagdown\diagup Y$
> Valency $3\diagdown\diagup 2$
>
> Therefore: X must be 3, therefore Group 3 or 5 : only Al (box A) is possible
>   Y must be 2, therefore Group 2 or 6 : only O (box E) is possible

2. A seemingly straightforward question made more difficult in that for part (b) the data booklet needs to be consulted and the question does not remind you of this.

2. (*a*) E and F (both needed for **1 mark**)

HINT
Covalent compounds are normally between 2 non-metals.

(*b*) C

HINT
Alkalis are formed when metal oxides dissolve in water.

Before answering this we must check that they dissolve in water by using the data booklet (p5).

We see that it can**not** be B (FeO) as it is insoluble.

3. An experiment where you have to analyse the effect of changes on the rate and the volume of gas made, knowing that all of the Mg reacts.

3. C: less Mg so less gas formed.

E: Mg ribbon instead of powder so slower.

HINT

In the answer 4 things are altered:

Mass of Mg

Particle Size of Mg (surface area)

Temperature

Concentration of acid

As all the Mg reacts: temperature, concentration and surface area have no effect on volume of gas made, they only effect how quickly it is made:

Higher temp/concentration/surface area : reaction faster : slope steeper than 1

Lower temp/concentration/surface area : reaction slower : slope less steep than 1

Mass of Mg does not affect rate but does affect final volume as less Mg reacts and so less gas is made.

Take each statement in turn, identify the 1 change made.

Ask what effect does this have.

Check if this is true for the graph.

i.e.   A: lower concentration: should be slower but graph is faster.

B: lower temperature: should be slower but same volume.

C: less mass of Mg: should give less gas. Therefore is correct

D: higher temperature: should be faster but graph is slower.

E: Mg ribbon (lower S.A.):   should be slower but same volume:

Correct

4. If In this question you needed to take your time and carefully consider each response. It is easy to jump to the incorrect answer.

4. C and D

 HINT

When diluting, we lower the concentration of H^+ ions so the pH moves towards 7, i.e. up (less acidic, but still acidic) and the reaction is slower as the concentration is lower.

The number of ions does not change so E and F are incorrect.

There are still more H^+ ions than OH^- ions so B is incorrect.

TOP EXAM TIP

When a substance becomes **less** acidic the pH **increases**.

If asked what happens to the pH, it is often better to answer that it moves **towards 7** (neutral)

 5. This question is based on the knowledge that metals reacting is oxidation and a compound reacting to form a metal is reduction.

5. A and D

HINT

Take each description in turn and deduce what it tells you about the reactivity of X

A X > Zn as it displaces zinc

B X > Ni as it is more readily oxidised

C X > Cu as the compound of X is more stable

D X > Fe as it is more reactive with acid

E X < Mg as its compounds are more easily reduced.

The order should be Mg > **X** > Zn > Fe > Ni > Cu

Therefore A and D tell us that **X** has been put in the wrong place.

TOP EXAM TIP

All metals want to lose electrons

When a metal reacts, it loses electrons, to obtain the electron arrangement of their nearest Noble Gas.

The more reactive a metal, the more readily it is oxidised.

The more reactive a metal, the less reactive (more stable) its compounds.

 6. A question requiring you to use the data book to find insoluble salts.

6. (*a*) A

HINT This is the only insoluble substance from the grid, on p5 of the data booklet.

(*b*) C and D (both needed for **1 mark**)

HINT

Go through each substance and see if the metal combining with the non-metal gives an insoluble substance.

The only insoluble salt possible is zinc carbonate.

7. This question asks you to relate the bonding and structure to the properties of MP/BP and electrical conductivity.

7. (*a*) E

HINT

$25°C$ must be above the MP and below the BP

i.e. on a number line

MP	25°C	BP

(*b*) B

HINT

Ionic: do not conduct when solid but do when liquid

Also have high MP and BP

(*c*) F

HINT

Covalent Network: never conduct electricity

but high MP and BP

8. A complicated question which you need to think about carefully and work out what ions are present and what is happening to each of them.

HINT

To do this question it is first easier to put the ions into the equation.

$$Cu^{2+}SO_4^{2-} + 4K^+I^- \longrightarrow 2Cu^+I^- + I_2 + 2(K^+)_2SO_4^{2-}$$

The difficult part is the Cu^{2+} and Cu^+.

Remember that the charges in a compound balance so the SO_4^{2-} and I^- help us deduce the charges on the other ions.

8. (*a*) D

HINT

Oxidation is loss of electrons.

Electrons are negatively charged.

So in oxidation the substance becomes less negative (–) or more positive (+).

$$4I^- \longrightarrow 2I^- + I_2.$$

So $2I^- \longrightarrow I_2$ It is becoming less (–) more (+).

TOP EXAM TIP

The equations on p7 of the data booklet are all reduction.

i.e. $I_2 + 2e^- \longrightarrow 2I^-$

If your equation is the reverse of this

i.e. $2I^- \longrightarrow I_2 + 2e^-$

then it must be the reverse of Reduction, i.e. Oxidation.

(b) B and C (both neded for **1 mark**)

> **HINT** Spectator ions remain unchanged. B and C are the only ions the same on both sides of the equation.

9. This question involves knowing that corrosion is oxidation and that metals in the electrochemical series give electrons to metals below them.

Thus the higher metals prevent corrosion but corrode faster themselves (sacrificial protection).

Metals low in the electrochemical series protect other metals by acting as a barrier to oxygen and water.

9. D and E

> **HINT**
>
> A Incorrect: Cu below iron and zinc above iron. So Cu Barrier, Zn Sacrificial
>
> B Incorrect: Zn is above Fe so electrons would flow from Zn to Fe
>
> C Incorrect: Zn above Fe in electrochemical series so oxidise (corrodes) faster.
>
> D/E Correct: Zn higher than Fe so it is oxidised and gives electrons to iron and so sacrifices itself.

10. This question tests knowledge of isotopes and covalent bonding.

10. (a) Isotopes are:

atoms with the same number of protons but different number of neutrons

OR atoms with the same Atomic Number but different Mass Number

(b) There must be the same amount of each isotope.

> **HINT** As the relative atomic mass is exactly midway between the Mass Number of both isotopes, it is not closer to either of them so they must exist in the ratio 1 : 1, i.e. 50% $^{79}_{35}$ Br and 50% $^{80}_{35}$ Br

(c)

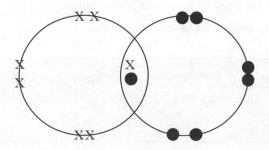

> **HINT** Bromine has 7 outer electrons (data booklet p1), so each atom shares 1 electron.

(d) In a covalent bond the negatively charged shared electrons are attracted to both positively charged nuclei.

> **HINT**
>
> A diagram helps to explain the answer to this question

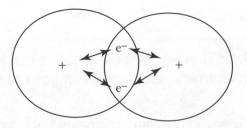

(e) 158, 160, 162

> **HINT**
>
> Bromine is Br$_2$ but for each Br we have a choice of two isotopes.
>
> ^{79}Br and ^{79}Br gives mass 158
>
> ^{79}Br and ^{81}Br gives mass 160
>
> ^{81}Br and ^{81}Br gives mass 162

11. Crude oil is separated by fractional distillation.

11. (a) Naphtha

> **HINT**
>
> When thinking of the fraction remember that they overlap.
>
> Octane is found in petrol which is the second top fraction. Octane has 8 C atoms.

(b) Gas oil contains larger molecules than naphtha and boiling point increases as the size of the molecule increases.

(c) (i) Fractions which are surplus (i.e. we have too much of) are cracked to give fractions which are in demand (i.e. we do not have enough of).

> **HINT**
>
> It is also good to describe cracking as breaking down large molecules to give more of the smaller, more useful, molecules.

(ii) It allows the reaction to happen at a lower temperature.

> **HINT**
>
> Do **not** answer this question in terms of saving money.
>
> It **must** be that a lower temperature can be used.

12. This question is mainly on graph drawing and analysis. It is made more difficult by being in a context which is not covered in Standard Grade.

12. (a)

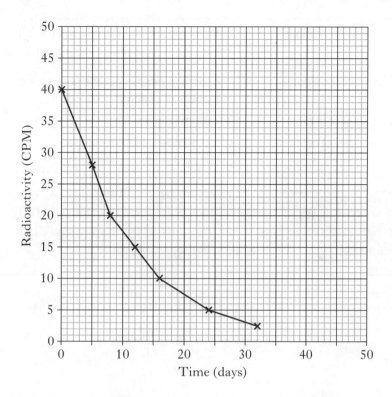

Answer

Y axis labelled radioactivity (CPM)

X axis labelled Time (days)   ($\frac{1}{2}$ mark)

Each large box on both axis worth 5 (therefore each box same value) ($\frac{1}{2}$ mark)

Points plotted (taking up more than $\frac{1}{2}$ the graph)   ($\frac{1}{2}$ mark)

Points joined to give a curve   ($\frac{1}{2}$ mark)

(b) 8 days

> **HINT**
>
> We are looking for the time of radioactivity to halve.
>
> From your graph 40 cpm to 20 cpm: 8 days
>
> 20 cpm to 10 cpm: 8 days
>
> This can also be worked out from the table.

(c) It would spend less time in the patient's body.

> **HINT**
>
> This question is very difficult. You need to look at the information in the question and then think of a reason for this advantage.

(d)

Particle	Number
proton	53
neutron	78

13. This question uses alkenes to look at your knowledge of reactions, isomers and polymers. It asks you to apply this knowledge to solve problems.

13. (*a*)

$$
\begin{array}{ccccccc}
 & H & Br & Br & H & \\
 & | & | & | & | & \\
H- & C- & C- & C- & C- & H \\
 & | & | & | & | & \\
 & H & H & H & H &
\end{array}
$$

HINT

When alkenes react the double bond is broken and the reacting chemical (i.e. bromine) is added to each carbon.

$$
\begin{array}{ccccccc}
H & H & H & H \\
| & | & | & | \\
H-C-C=C-C-H & + & Br-Br \\
| & & | \\
H & & H
\end{array}
\longrightarrow
\begin{array}{cccc}
H & Br & Br & H \\
| & | & | & | \\
H-C-C-C-C-H \\
| & | & | & | \\
H & H & H & H
\end{array}
$$

(*b*)
$$
\begin{array}{cc}
H_2C-CH_2 \\
| \quad\quad | \\
H_2C-CH_2
\end{array}
\quad \text{and} \quad
\begin{array}{c}
H \quad H \\
| \quad | \\
H-C-C-CH_3 \\
\diagdown \diagup \\
H-C-H
\end{array}
\quad \text{are both possible}
$$

HINT

Cycloalkanes are saturated isomers of alkenes and do not reach with bromine.

(*c*) Addition polymers are based on ethene so we must make it look like ethene

$$
\begin{array}{cc}
H \quad H \\
| \quad | \\
C=C \\
| \quad | \\
H \quad H
\end{array}
$$
i.e. like a set of rugby posts

$$
\begin{array}{cc}
| \quad | \\
C=C \\
| \quad |
\end{array}
$$

To get the structure for this question, put the methyl groups on each end

$$
\begin{array}{cccc}
H & & & H \\
| & & & | \\
H-C+C=C+C-H \\
| & | & | & | \\
H & H & H & H
\end{array}
$$

Then write them as CH$_3$ and move them to the top.

$$\begin{array}{cc}
CH_3 & CH_3 \\
| & | \\
C & = C \\
| & | \\
H & H
\end{array}$$

And the polymer is

$$\begin{array}{cccccc}
CH_3 & CH_3 & CH_3 & CH_3 & CH_3 & CH_3 \\
| & | & | & | & | & | \\
-C- & C- & C- & C- & C- & C- \\
| & | & | & | & | & | \\
H & H & H & H & H & H
\end{array}$$

14. This question takes plant food as a basis for asking questions from a number of units and includes an unusual table for problem solving.

14. (a) FeSO$_4$

HINT

The roman numerals tell us that the valency of iron is 2
Page 4 of the data booklet tells us that sulphate is SO$_4^{2-}$, the valency is 2
Fe $\quad$ SO$_4$ giving Fe$_2$(SO$_4$)$_2$ which cancels to FeSO$_4$

$\quad$ 2 $\qquad$ 2

This could also have been done by putting on the charges

Iron(II) is Fe^{2+}, sulphate is SO$_4^{2-}$
Therefore Fe^{2+}SO$_4^{2-}$ charges cancel, so this is the correct formula

We were not asked for the ionic formula so we do not need charges.

(b) 28·2%

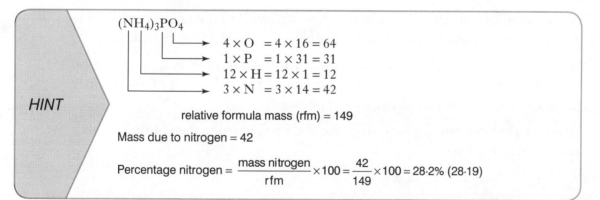

HINT

(NH$_4$)$_3$PO$_4$

$4 \times O = 4 \times 16 = 64$
$1 \times P = 1 \times 31 = 31$
$12 \times H = 12 \times 1 = 12$
$3 \times N = 3 \times 14 = 42$

relative formula mass (rfm) = 149

Mass due to nitrogen = 42

Percentage nitrogen = $\dfrac{\text{mass nitrogen}}{\text{rfm}} \times 100 = \dfrac{42}{149} \times 100 = 28\cdot2\%$ (28·19)

(c) (i) The reaction is reversible.

HINT

The reversible arrows ($\rightleftharpoons$) show that the reaction goes backwards as well as forward so some of the product (ammonia) will always be turned back into reactant (nitrogen and hydrogen).

(ii) As pressure increases, the percentage of ammonia produced increases.

HINT

Take one temperature from the table and look at the effect of pressure on the percentage of ammonia produced.

(iii) At lower temperatures the reaction is too slow.

 HINT | Although a lower temperature gives a larger percentage of ammonia, the reaction is so slow that more ammonia is actually produced <u>per day</u> at 500°C as the reaction is happening more quickly.

★ **15.** This problem solving question requires you to think back to reactions which produce carbon dioxide and evidence for ions.

15. (a) Carbonate.

HINT | Think about the reactions of acids where carbonates give us carbon dioxide.

(b) The best answer here would be electrolysis, where copper colour would be produced at the negative electrode.

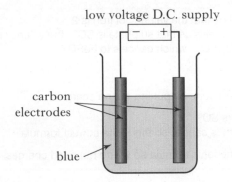

low voltage D.C. supply

carbon electrodes

blue

This is a good answer because

(i) copper ions are positive and would be attracted to the negative electrode forming copper metal, which is visible.

(ii) the blue colour due to copper ions would disappear and the solution would become colourless and stop conducting when all of the copper ions had been reduced to give copper metal.

Another possible answer is to displace the copper from the solution with a more reactive metal.

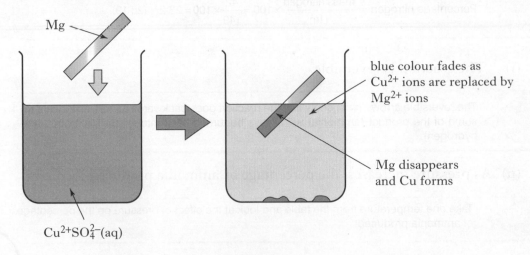

Mg

blue colour fades as Cu^{2+} ions are replaced by Mg^{2+} ions

Mg disappears and Cu forms

$Cu^{2+}SO_4^{2-}(aq)$

16. This question on titration starts with a simple question which some people get incorrect because it seems too obvious and easy. There is also a calculation.

16. (a) Indicator

HINT Do not expect all of the answers to be complicated, some can be obvious.

(b) 0·2 mol/l

HINT

Do this in 4 steps

1) Try to calculate what you are asked (concentration of NaOH)

2) If something is missing, work out the number of moles of the other substance, H_2SO_4.

3) Use the balanced equation to work out how many moles of NaOH.

4) Knowing the number of moles of NaOH, calculate the concentration.

   1) The concentration of NaOH

      To do this we use $c = n/v$ we know v = 20cm³ = 20/100 = 0·020 l

                                             but we do not know n (no.of moles)

   2) We have the concentration and volume of H_2SO_4 so we can work out the

      number of moles of H_2SO_4

      $n = c \times v = 0.1 \times 0.02 = 0.020$ moles

   3) We can now use the balanced equation to work out the number of moles of

      NaOH as the ratio of H_2SO_4 : NaOH is 1 : 2

                    H_2SO_4 : 2NaOH

                    1 mol : 2 mol

                    0·002mol : 0·004 mol

   4) We can now work out the concentration of NaOH

      Therefore $c = n/v = 0.004/0.02 = 0.2$ mol/l

   This can be summarised and presented as:

   $$H_2SO_4 \quad + \quad 2NaOH \longrightarrow Na_2SO_4 + 2\,H_2O$$

                                    $c = n/v$

                                    $= n/0.020$ (½ mark)

   $n = c \times v$

      $= 0.1 \times 0.020$

      $= 0.0020$ mol   : $n = 0.0040$ mol (½ mark)

      (½ mark) $c = 0.0040/0.020$

                             $= \mathbf{0.2\ mol/l}$ (½ mark)

17. This question uses displacement to ask a number of problem-solving questions.

17. (*a*) As metals become further from aluminium in the electrochemical series the temperature change increases.

OR The closer the metals are to aluminium, the lower the temperature increase.

HINT

You had to refer to the data booklet page 7

Look at where the metals copper, nickel, iron and zinc are in the electrochemical series compared to aluminium.

(*b*) Any temperature above 61°C

HINT

Silver is below copper. The final temperature must be higher than with copper.

The temperature changes in the table are

copper	41
nickel	28
iron (II)	20
zinc (II)	11

A sensible change would be around 50°C giving the answer of 70°C

(*c*) The volume of the solution

The concentration of the solution

HINT

The aluminium is in excess, ensuring all solutions are displaced. So its mass and particle size do not matter as they only affect how quickly the final temperature is reached, not the actual final temperature.

The starting temperature does not matter because we are measuring a rise in temperature not the actual temperature.

(*d*) Cu^{2+} ions are gaining electrons to become Cu.

HINT

The formation of any metal is reduction.

Data book (p7) of reduction reactions shows this reaction.

18. This question requires you to know the relative sizes of molecules and the difference between condensation and hydrolysis. The problem-solving part needs to be tackled carefully.

18. (*a*) The molecules are smaller. They can get into the blood stream quickly.

(*b*) Condensation

HINT

Joining by removing water is called condensation

(*c*) It needs to be broken down.

HINT

Starch is too big a molecule to get from the gut into the bloodstream without being broken down (hydrolysed).

TOP EXAM TIP

Get the following meanings clear in your head.

Hydration   adding water

Dehydration   removing water

Hydrolysis   **breaking down** by adding water

Condensation   **joining** by removing water

(d) It indicates that glucose contains carbon and hydrogen.

HINT

On burning, a substance is reacting with and joining to oxygen.

CO_2 is produced so carbon (C) must have been present

H_2O is produced so hydrogen (H) must have been present.

Note the temptation was to answer that oxygen is present, as we should know that carbohydrates contain carbon, hydrogen and oxygen.

However, the oxygen in CO_2 and H_2O may have come from the air so we cannot say that glucose contains oxygen.

19. This problem-solving question requires you to look carefully at the structures, analyse their reactions and think carefully about the definition of a Homologous Series.

19. (a) In aldehydes the carbonyl group is at the end of the molecule.

In ketones the carbonyl is in the middle (i.e. not at the end) of the molecule.

(b) (i) Aldehydes give a silver mirror with Tollens' reagent.
Silver ions are being reduced, so the aldehyde must be being oxidised.
As ketones do not react, they are not being oxidised.

TOP EXAM TIP

Oxidation and reduction always go together.

A substance cannot lose electrons unless another substance accepts them.

Likewise, a substance cannot gain electrons unless another substance loses them.

(ii) They have different chemical reactions. (i.e. aldehydes can be oxidised).

HINT

Homologous series must have all three of:

Same general formula

Similar chemical properties

Gradual change in physical properties.

1. This question is testing your knowledge of the charges on atomic particles and is made slightly harder by referring to energy levels as opposed to electron levels.

1. (*a*) A + C (both needed for **1 mark**)

HINT
> Protons have a positive charge.
> Electrons have a negative charge.
>
> Atoms are neutral, so there must be the same number of protons and electrons in order for the charges to cancel out.

(*b*) A + B (both needed for **1 mark**)

HINT
> Mass Number = number of protons + number of neutrons

(*c*) C, D   **1 mark** each

HINT
> Na 2,8,1   loses 1 electron giving Na^+ 2,8
> F 2,7   gains 1 electron giving F^- 2,8

 2. A straightforward question requiring you to know that alkenes are unsaturated. You must be able to apply formulae to names with a knowledge of cracking.

2. (*a*) A + C   (both needed for **1 mark**)

HINT
> Alkenes are unsaturated.

(*b*) A + B   (both needed for **1 mark**)

HINT
> The easiest way to do this is to check the number of carbons. Only A and B have the same number (6 carbons).
>
> This is confirmed, as alkenes and cycloalkanes are isomers of each other.

TOP EXAM TIP

If you cannot remember how many carbon atoms hydrocarbons have, use the data booklet (p6). The table of MP and BP in the middle on the left lists the alkanes in order of the number of carbons from methane (1 carbon) to octane (8 carbons).

(*c*) C + D   (both needed for **1 mark**)

HINT
> Cracking produces smaller molecules, so they must have fewer carbons than pentane (5).
> One of the products is always an alkene, so cyclobutane is not possible.

TOP EXAM TIP

Cracking alkanes always produces an alkane **and** an alkene.

3. A problem-solving question requiring you to know the charges on ions and what is moving when a substance conducts electricity.

3. C, D (**1 mark** each)

HINT

Metals give positive charged ions so the nickel (green) will be attracted to the negative electrode (B).

At the negative electrode (B), electrons are supplied and we get reduction so nickel (the metal) will be formed.

Sulphate ions are negative (see the data booklet p4) and are attracted to the positive electrode (A), therefore A remains colourless.

Ions move through solutions, electrons move through metals (i.e. the leads connecting the electrodes to the power pack).

TOP EXAM TIP

Use the areas in bold to help you remember what is moving when a substance conducts electricity.

electrons move through metals   **e**lectrons move through m**e**tals

ions move through solutions   **ion**s move through solut**ion**s

4. A question on pH which requires you to know the definition of neutral and the ionic nature of salts.

4. (*a*) E

HINT

Go through each answer and see if it applies to both water and potassium chloride.

(*b*) A, B (**1 mark** each)

HINT

Aluminium cannot displace potassium from its solution so there is no reaction in B

Potassium chloride is ionic so will give chlorine when electrolysed.

5. This question use water as the basis for testing knowledge over several topics.

5. (*a*) F

HINT

Remember the 4 reactions of acids which form a salt. (see page 113)

(b) B and C (**1 mark** each)

> B and C are the only equations where water is removed from a compound.
>
> In A, D and F it is made as the result of a reaction.
>
> In E it is one of the reactants.

(c) B

> HINT
>
> This is the only equation where a product fits the general formula of the alkenes (C_nH_{2n}).

⭐ **6.** This question asks you to identify types of reactions.

---

6. (a) B and E (**1 mark** each)

> HINT
>
> Glucose molecules are joined by removing water: condensation.
> Starch is a polymer, therefore the reaction is also polymerisation.

(b) C and F (**1 mark** each)

> Zinc is displacing the ions of copper which is lower in the electrochemical series.
>
> The zinc atoms are being turned into zinc ions: oxidation
>
> The copper ions are being turned into copper atoms: reduction
>
> Therefore displacement is also a REDOX reaction.

⭐ **7.** This question starts off with a very straightforward question and moves into an explanation of ionic structure and properties, where you must be very clear.

---

7. (a) To achieve a stable electron arrangement

> HINT
>
> You could use the words: stable octet, 8 outer electrons, (2 for the smaller atoms), electron arrangement of the nearest Noble Gas, but to get the full mark you must mention that a **stable** electron arrangement is achieved.

(b) They exist in a lattice with a large number (= **mark**)
     of very strong bonds between oppositely charged ions (= **mark**)

(c) (i)   The ions cannot move in the solid. (= **mark**)

          The ions can move when in solution. (= **mark**)

> HINT
>
> Ionic substances conduct by the movement of ions carrying the charge.
>
> In the solid the ions are held in the lattice and cannot move.

TOP EXAM TIP

NEVER talk about electrons when explaining why ionic substances conduct.

ALWAYS talk about the movement of IONS.

(ii) $2 \text{ Cl}^- \longrightarrow \text{Cl}_2 + 2e^-$

HINT

You are told that chlorine (Cl$_2$) is formed.

Turn to page 7 of the data booklet, find the equation and turn it around so that the Cl$_2$ is on the right.

Also: the ions are attracted to the positive electrode.

We always get oxidation at the positive electrode.

Data booklet p7 is reduction reactions, so find the equation and turn it around to get oxidation.

TOP EXAM TIP

reaction at:

Negative	Electrode	Reduction
Positive	Electrode	Oxidation

Data booklet p7 is Reduction reactions.

8. A simple question to start an unusual question on graph drawing.

8. (*a*) To improve the properties of metals.

HINT

Alloys are mixtures of metals to improve their properties.
For example stainless steel is an alloy of iron which does not rust.

(*b*)

Graph: Light passing through solution (%) (y-axis, 0 to 100) against Concentration of permanganate ions (mol/l) (x-axis, 0 to 2·0).

Labels with units ½ **mark**

Concentration of permanganate ions (mol/l)   X-axis

Light passing through solution (%)   Y-axis

Scale   ½ **mark**
You must take up at least half the graph paper.

Plot points correctly   ½ **mark**

Join points   ½ **mark**
Best fit line (here a curve)
Or join the points

HINT Get the labels and units from the table of results.

TOP EXAM TIP

To choose a scale think of coins which we spend:

1p   2p   5p   10p   20p   50p   £1(100p)

The number on your axis should normally be based on these.

In Q8 of practice paper D

each large box on X- axis is 0·2   (based on 2p)
each large box on Y-axis is 10   (based on 10p)

The other number which can be used is 25, based on the American coin the 'quarter' (25 cents).

(c)   As permanganate concentration increases, the percentage of light passing through decreases.

OR As permanganate concentration decreases, the percentage of light passing through increases.

(d) 0·96 mol/l

HINT this mark depends on what it actually says on the graph you draw.

---

 9. Another calculation which requires use of a balanced equation. The question is on the metal topic but manages to bring in questions from the topics on fuels and acids.

(a) Platinum is an unreactive metal.

HINT The easier a metal is to get from its compound, the less stable the compound and so the less reactive the metal.

(b) There are 3 methods of doing calculations

<u>Method 1</u>

Do the question in 4 parts, each worth ½ **mark**.

1) Try to work out what you are asked; the mass of sulphur dioxide (SO_2).

2) Work out the number of moles of the substance you are told about, NiS.

3) Use the balanced equation to work out how many moles of SO_2 this will make.

4) Knowing the number of moles of SO_2, calculate the mass using the mass triangle.

1) Work out the mass of SO_2.
   Use the triangle below when talking about masses.

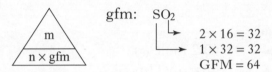

gfm: SO_2

$2 \times 16 = 32$
$1 \times 32 = 32$
GFM = 64

mass of SO_2 = n × gfm

mass of SO_2 = n × 64

We do not know 'n' so work out 'n' from the substance we are told about, i.e. NiS.

2) Work out the number of moles of NiS.

number of moles of NiS: n = m/gfm

mass = 18·1g

gfm: NiS

$1 \times 32 = 32$
$1 \times 58·5 = 58·5$
GFM = 90·5

m = n/gfm = 18·1/90·5 = 0·2 mole

3) Use the balanced equation to work out how many moles of sulphur dioxide this will make.

$$2NiS + 3O_2 \longrightarrow 2NiO + 2SO_2$$

balanced

equation tells   2 moles   makes   2 moles

therefore   0·2 mole   will make   0·2 moles

4) Knowing the number of moles of SO_2, calculate the mass using the mass triangle.

m = n × GFM = 0·2 × 64 = 12·8g

Method 2

As method 1 but set out differently

$$2NiS + 3O_2 \longrightarrow 2NiO + 2SO_2$$

$$m = n \times gfm$$
$$= n \times 64 \; (=)$$

SO_2
$\quad 2 \times 16 = 32$
$\quad 1 \times 32 = 32$
$\quad gfm \quad = 64$

NiS
$\quad 1 \times 32 \; = 32$
$\quad 1 \times 58 \cdot 5 = 58 \cdot 5$
$\quad gfm = \overline{90 \cdot 5}$

$$n = \frac{m}{gfm}$$
$$= \frac{18 \cdot 1}{90 \cdot 5}$$

this will make

$= 0 \cdot 2$ mole $\longrightarrow$ $0 \cdot 2$ mole $(=)$
$(\frac{1}{2})$ $\qquad\qquad\qquad\qquad m = n \times gfm$
$\qquad\qquad\qquad\qquad = 0 \cdot 2 \times 1 \cdot 4$
$\qquad\qquad\qquad\qquad = 12 \cdot 8g \; (=)$

Method 3

using gfm, the balanced equation and direct proportion

$$2NiS + 3O_2 \longrightarrow 2NiO + 2SO_2$$

Using GFM $\quad 2(90 \cdot 5)g \; (\frac{1}{2} \textbf{ mark})$ $\qquad\qquad\qquad 2(64g) \; (\frac{1}{2} \textbf{ mark})$
So $\qquad\qquad 181g$ $\qquad\qquad\qquad\qquad\qquad 128g \; (\frac{1}{2} \textbf{ mark})$
Therefore $\quad 18 \cdot 1g$ $\qquad\qquad\qquad\qquad\qquad 12 \cdot 8g \; (\frac{1}{2} \textbf{ mark})$

(c) It produces sulphur dioxide, which is a cause of acid rain.

(d) (i) Catalytic convertors turn hamful gases into less harmful gases.
(ii) This increases the surface area.

HINT   The above answer is what is looked for. It may be useful to say that there is therefore more contact with the gases and so more are turned into less harmful gases.

10. This question asks some simple questions on alkanes and cracking, but people often find it hard to put in words what they know in their head.

10. (a) (i) C_5H_{12}

HINT   This is another way of asking you to balance an equation.
The number of atoms of each element (i.e. C and H) must be the same on each side of the equation.

(ii) There are not enough hydrogen atoms to form alkanes only,

HINT   People tend to know the answer to this question but do not know how to say it. The above answer should get you the mark.

(b) C_nH_{2n}

(c) $96 - 120°C$

HINT

Look for a trend in BP increase in the data book (p6). Both tables of BP of alkenes give the same values. (The Standard Grade table and the Intermediate 2 table)

The biggest temp increase is 57°C and the smallest increase is 33°C.

Therefore adding between 33 and 57 to the BP of hex –1-ene gives any number between 96 and 120 as acceptable.

11. This is a difficult question asking you to carefully transfer information in a passage onto a diagram which will work. It also asks you to relate type of bonding to the properties rather than to the elements present.

11. (*a*) (i) Complete and label the diagram to show how tin (IV) chloride can be formed.

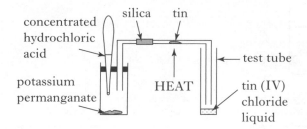

Drawing: for 1 mark you need all of the following.

Stopper in test tube

Delivery tube leaving test tube

If either is omitted the experiment will not work (i.e. if stopper is omitted the chlorine will escape) therefore no mark.

Labels: for ½ **mark** each; potassium permanganate, tin

(ii) covalent

HINT

Although it has a metal, it is not ionic bonding as it is a liquid.

TOP EXAM TIP

When deciding on the type of bond the basic rule is:

metal/non-metal: ionic

non-metal/non-metal: covalent

but we also need to look at the properties if they are given:

	covalent	ionic
conducts electricity	never	when melted/dissolved
MP/BP	network: high molecule: low	high

Therefore if a substance does not conduct or has a low MP/BP (i.e. solid or liquid at room temperature) it **must** be **covalent.**

(*b*) The double bond is being broken and the monomer molecules are joining (being added to) each other to form a polymer.

HINT

You must mention the double bond being broken and the molecules joining together.

12. This question on cells covers many topics including direction of electron flow, oxidation, reduction, the use of suitable ion bridges and a knowledge of ions in acids.

12. (*a*) By a chemical reaction

> **HINT** This answer is so obvious that people often do not want to put it as it looks too simple.

(*b*)

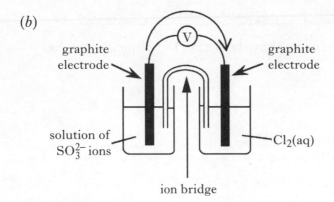

graphite electrode

graphite electrode

solution of SO_3^{2-} ions

$Cl_2(aq)$

ion bridge

> **HINT** The sulphite ions are losing electrons.
>
> Therefore electrons move from sulphite to chlorine.
>
> NOTE: The electrons must flow through the wire, as only ions move in solutions.
>
> ALWAYS: put the electrons above the meter.

(*c*) Electrons are being lost.

> **HINT** As the electrons are on the right-hand side, they are being lost by the sulphite and are left over.

TOP EXAM TIP

If you are getting confused about oxidation or reduction, remember it using:

OILRIG   Oxidation Is Loss Reduction Is Gain

Or   LEO the lion says GER

LEO   Loss Electrons Oxidation

GER   Gain Electrons Reduction

You can also look at p7 of the data book which are all reduction equations.
The electrons are on the left as they are being added (gained).

(*d*) The pH would go down (become acidic).

> **HINT** Looking at the equation, H^+ ions are being formed and this makes it acidic.

(*e*) $Cl_2 + 2e^- \longrightarrow 2Cl^-$

> **HINT** As the equation in the left-hand beaker is oxidation, the equation here must be reduction. So turn to p7 and copy the equation for the reduction of chlorine.

(f) The silver ions will form a solid (precipitate) with the chloride ions (data booklet p5) and so will not be able to conduct and the cell will stop working.

TOP EXAM TIP

Silver compounds are very poor choices for ion bridges as most of their salts are insoluble.

---

13. This question starts simply but then comes on to a calculation which although part of the course has not been assessed in recent years. The final part, although pure knowledge, is often overlooked.

13. (a) water and oxygen (air)

> **HINT** Although at Credit level you should know that an electrolyte is also needed for rusting (to allow conduction), if asked for two things always give the answer above.

(b) FeO_2H_2 (elements in any order) or $Fe(OH)_2$

> **HINT**
>
> In this question you are working out the number of moles of each element in a compound and then using the ratio to get the formula.
>
> Use 4 steps
>
> 1) Calculate the mass of each element
>
>   (If given %, assume sample weighs 100g (Therefore 10% will be 10g.)
>
> 2) Work out the number of moles of each element.
>
> 3) Work out the ratio of each atom.
>
>   (divide them all by the smallest number of moles)
>
> 4) Write the formula
>
> | | Fe | O | H | |
> |---|---|---|---|---|
> | | 62·3% | 35·5% | 2·2% | |
> | mass | 62·3g | 35·5g | 2·2g | ½ **mark** |
> | number of moles $n = m/gfm$ | 62·3/56 | 35·5/16 | 2·2/1 | |
> | | = 1·1 | = 2·2 | 2·2 | ½ **mark** |
> | ratio (divide by smallest) | 1·1/1·1 | 2·2/1·1 | 2·2/1·1 | |
> | | 1: | 2 | 2 | ½ **mark** |
> | formula | FeO_2H_2 or $Fe(OH)_2$ | | | ½ **mark** |

(c) Fe^{3+}

> **HINT** It is often overlooked that rusting produces Fe^{2+} **and** Fe^{3+}.

14. A problem-solving based question which also requires some precise knowledge of salts.

14. (*a*) Unreacted nitrogen and hydrogen is recycled into the process.

(*b*) Cool the mixture to turn the ammonia into a liquid/condensation of ammonia.

HINT: The BPs of hydrogen and nitrogen are very low. (Data booklet pages 3 and 6). If the mixture of ammonia/nitrogen/hydrogen is cooled, the ammonia will turn into a liquid first, leaving the gases to be recycled.

(*c*) $4NH_3 + 5O_2 \longrightarrow 4NO + 6H_2O$

(*d*) (i) The hydrogen ion of the acid has been replaced with a metal ion.

HINT: This is the definition of a salt in Credit chemistry.

(ii) Heat the solution to evaporate the water and leave the solid salt.

15. This question asks you to look for a trend and then look at the question to suggest why the result of an experiment may be different from that which is expected.

15. (*a*) −3534 to −3546 kJ/mol

HINT: The changes in enthalpies of combustion are 669, 660, 657.

So we would expect the next change to be an increase of between 657 and 669, giving any answer between the two temperatures as acceptable.

(*b*) In a gas cooker the methane is burned in air (not pure oxygen).

OR The methane in a gas cooker may have impurities.

HINT: This question is looking for a sensible answer which shows that you have thought of a difference between the definition of energy of combustion and what actually happens when methane is burned in a gas cooker.